PERGAMON INTERNATIONA
of Science, Technology, Engineering an
The 1000-volume original paperback library
industrial training and the enjoymen.
Publisher: Robert Maxwell, M.C.

ELASTO-HYDRODYNAMIC LUBRICATION
SI edition

International Series on
MATERIALS SCIENCE AND TECHNOLOGY
Volume 23—Editor: D. W. Hopkins

PERGAMON MATERIALS ADVISORY COMMITTEE

Other Titles in the International Series on
MATERIALS SCIENCE AND TECHNOLOGY

ELASTO-HYDRODYNAMIC LUBRICATION

SI Edition

by

D. DOWSON
The University of Leeds

and

G. R. HIGGINSON
The University of Durham

CHAPTERS 9 AND 10 BY

J. F. ARCHARD
The University of Leicester

and

A. W. CROOK
Brunel University

PERGAMON PRESS
OXFORD · NEW YORK · TORONTO
SYDNEY · PARIS · FRANKFURT

U.K.	Pergamon Press Ltd., Headington Hill Hall, Oxford OX3 0BW, England
U.S.A.	Pergamon Press Inc., Maxwell House, Fairview Park, Elmsford, New York 10523, U.S.A.
CANADA	Pergamon of Canada Ltd., 75 The East Mall, Toronto, Ontario, Canada
AUSTRALIA	Pergamon Press (Aust.) Pty. Ltd., 19a Boundary Street, Rushcutters Bay, N.S.W. 2011, Australia
FRANCE	Pergamon Press SARL, 24 rue des Ecoles, 75240 Paris, Cedex 05, France
WEST GERMANY	Pergamon Press GmbH, 6242 Kronberg-Taunus Pferdstrasse 1, Frankfurt-am-Main, West Germany

First edition 1966

SI edition 1977

Library of Congress Cataloging in Publication Data

Dowson, D.
Elasto-hydrodynamic lubrication. SI edition

Bibliography: p.
Includes indexes.
1. Roller bearings—Lubrication. 2. Gearing—
Lubrication. I. Higginson, G. R., joint author.
II. Title.
TJ1071.D64   1977   621.8'9   76–58388
ISBN 0-08-021303-0 (Hardcover)
ISBN 0-08-021302-2 (Flexicover)

Printed in Great Britain by Biddles Ltd., Guildford, Surrey

CONTENTS

PREFACE TO SECOND EDITION

APART from a few very minor alterations, this second edition differs from the first only in the units, which are SI. In many cases the equivalent Imperial values are given alongside the SI figures, but that has not been overdone. In particular, only the SI unit of viscosity, the Pa s $\equiv$ Ns/m^2, is given, because it differs from the c.g.s. unit, the poise, merely by a factor of 10 (1 Pa s $\equiv$ 10 P); the Imperial and other units of dynamic viscosity are rarely seen in the technical literature and are not used at all in this new edition.

The special name pascal (Pa) has been used generally for the SI unit of pressure and stress, N/m^2; and the prefixes G (giga 10^9), M (mega 10^6), k (kilo 10^3), m (milli 10^{-3}), μ (micro 10^{-6}), n (nano 10^{-9}) and p (pico 10^{-12}) have been freely used.

PREFACE TO FIRST EDITION

THIS research monograph is about elasto-hydrodynamic lubrication, the name given to the lubrication regime in operation over the small areas where machine components are in nominal point or line contact. The lubrication mechanism is fundamentally the same as in a journal bearing, where the area of the lubricated surfaces is large, but the conditions are much more severe; in particular the pressure which must be generated in the lubricant is very much higher.

Gears and rolling-contact bearings, and no doubt many other contacting machine elements, have enjoyed hydrodynamic lubrication for very many years, but only during the last fifteen or so has this been recognized, and only during the last few years has the classical lubrication theory been sufficiently modified to be reconciled with practical observations in this field. The theory still has far to go to become anything like complete, but recent experiments have shown that it has already advanced far enough to be of some use to engineering designers.

This monograph has been written by four men who, although at the time the work was done were two pairs, at the time of writing were in four different places. They have tried to produce a unified document, but they apologize in advance for any discontinuities which the reader may detect.

The authors would like to thank Thornton (Shell) Research Centre, particularly Dr. H. Naylor, for providing information on lubricant properties, much of it elusive, over a period of several years; and Mr. A. V. Whitaker, of Leeds University, for computing many of the later results described in Chapter 7.

NOTATION

SYMBOLS which only arise once, and are defined on the spot, are not listed.

$2b$ width of Hertzian contact zone

$$\frac{b}{R} = 4 \left(\frac{W}{2\pi}\right)^{\frac{1}{4}} = 4P_0$$

C capacitance
C_D inter-specimen capacitance
C_F, C_S pad–disc capacitances
c specific heat

E internal energy
E e.m.f.
E_1, E_2 elastic moduli of solids in contact

$$\frac{1}{E'} = \frac{1}{2}\left[\frac{1 - \sigma_1^2}{E_1} + \frac{1 - \sigma_2^2}{E_2}\right]$$

e_x, e_y, e_z, e_{xy} strain components in solids

F surface shear force
$\bar{F}$ $F/2\eta u$
F' $F/E'R$
F_R surface shear force in pure rolling
F_s surface shear force due to sliding

G $\alpha E'$
G shear modulus

H h/R
h lubricant film thickness
h_m film thickness at point of maximum pressure
h_0 film thickness on line of centres

K $2/\pi E'$
k thermal conductivity

l	gear centre distance
L	.width of leading edge of electrode
M	W'/P_0'
N_1, N_2	speeds in r.p.m. of gear wheel and pinion
P	p/E'
P'	line load/unit length on solid surface
P_0	p_0/E'
$P_{0, 1, 2...}'$	load per unit length carried by individual rollers in a roller bearing assembly
P_0'	maximum load per unit length carried by most heavily loaded roller
P_x, P_y	hydrodynamic force components per unit length of cylinder
P_x'	$P_x/E'R$
$\bar{P}_x$, etc.	$P_x/2U$
p	pressure
p_0	Hertzian maximum pressure
$\left.\begin{array}{l} p_r, p_\theta, q_{r\theta} \\ p_x, p_y, q_{xy} \end{array}\right\}$	stresses in solids
Q	volume rate of flow of lubricant
$\underline{Q}$	q/E'
$\bar{Q}$	Q/uh_0, dimensionless flow rate
q	reduced pressure, defined by $q = (1 - e^{-\alpha p})/\alpha$
q	heat flow
R	effective radius of roller pair $= \dfrac{R_a R_b}{R_a \pm R_b}$
R_a, R_b	radii of cylinders or rollers in contact
R_1	radius of roller bearing inner race
R_1, R_2	pitch circle radii of gear wheels
R_g	gear ratio
r	radius of roller
r, θ, z	coordinates
S	R/h_0
s	additional coordinate in x-direction
s	r/R_1

s	distance between point of gear contact and pitch point
$s_{frac.}$	fractional distance along line of action of gears measured from base circle of wheel
U	$\eta_0 u / E' R$
u	$\frac{1}{2}(u_1 + u_2)$
u_1, u_2	surface velocities of solids in x-direction
u, v, w	fluid velocities in x-, y-, z-directions
u, v, w	solid displacements in x-, y-, z-directions
V	$\eta_0(u_1 - u_2) / E' R$
W	$w / E' R$
W'	total load per unit length on roller bearing $\left(= \dfrac{\text{total load on bearing}}{\text{length of } \textit{rollers}} \right)$
w	load per unit length of cylinder
X	x / b
x, y, z	coordinates
Z	total number of rollers in bearing
α	pressure exponent of viscosity, $\eta = \eta_0 \exp (\alpha p)$
α	$\dfrac{\omega_c}{\Omega} 2(1 + s)$
β	$\dfrac{\omega}{\Omega} \dfrac{2s(1 + s)}{(1 + 2s)}$
γ	temperature exponent of viscosity, $\eta = \eta_x \exp (-\gamma\theta)$
Δ	radial clearance in roller bearing
δ	deflection
ε	dielectric constant
ε	radial interference in roller bearing
η	viscosity
η_0	"controlling viscosity", viscosity at conditions of entry to contact
η_L	viscosity of lubricant at supply temperature
η_n	viscosity at ordinate where $du/dy = (u_2 - u_1)/h$
η_s	viscosity at solid surface temperature
θ	temperature

μ	coefficient of friction
ϱ	fluid density
ϱ_m	fluid density at point of max. pressure
ϱ_0	fluid density at conditions of entry to contact
σ_1, σ_2	Poisson's ratio
τ	tangential surface stress
φ	energy dissipation function
φ	stress function
ψ	pressure angle
Ω	angular velocity of bearing inner race
ω	angular velocity of a bearing roller about its centre relative to rotating axes
ω_c	angular velocity of bearing roller centre about shaft axis (cage speed)

CHAPTER 1

INTRODUCTION

IN MANY bearings and contacts forces are transmitted through thin, but continuous, fluid films which separate the solid machine components. The subject of hydrodynamic lubrication as applied to journal and thrust bearings of conventional proportions is well developed, and the confirmation of theoretical predictions by experiment has led to the development of satisfactory design procedures. A characteristic of conventional bearings is the high degree of geometrical conformity between the bearing components; a feature which enables substantial loads to be carried by relatively small oil film pressures.

The subject of *elasto-hydrodynamic lubrication* deals with the lubrication of elastic contacts. In recent years it has been recognized that many loaded contacts of low geometrical conformity such as gears, rolling contact bearings and cams frequently behave as though they are hydrodynamically lubricated. For some time these observations were at variance with theory, and it is only in the last few years that a fairly clear picture of the phenomenon has emerged. The contact conditions in many machines are now being re-examined and power transmission equipment is currently being designed to take advantage of the elasto-hydrodynamic concept.

Some of the assumptions employed in the analysis of normal fluid film bearings cannot be made in elasto-hydrodynamic theory. In particular the influence of high pressure on the viscosity of liquid lubricants is most marked, and the effect must be fully considered in an analysis of highly loaded lubricated contacts. Furthermore, the application of high contact loads can lead to substantial local deformation of the elastic solids; an effect which may drastically change the geometry of the lubricating film. Since the shape of the lubricant film in turn determines the pressure distribution, it is at once apparent that a solution to the elasto-hydrodynamic problem must simultaneously satisfy the governing elastic and lubrication equations. These basic equations are presented in Chapters 2 and 5, and by first considering the lubrication of rigid contacts and then introducing the effects of high pressure on the lubricant and bounding solids, the book is developed in a manner reminiscent of the history of the subject. Some of the steps taken in the short history of elasto-hydrodynamic lubrication will now be recalled.

A study of the contact conditions in gears provided most of the early interest in the possibility of fluid film lubrication in highly loaded contacts. Operating experience suggested that severe metal-to-metal contact was not taking place, and this led to a theoretical analysis of the lubrication conditions. One of the earliest solutions to the equivalent problem of the lubrication of a cylinder near a plane was presented by Martin (1916) in an unsigned article in Engineering. Martin considered rigid solids and an incompressible, isoviscous lubricant, and his extension of the standard Reynolds solution to a new geometry forms a convenient starting point. It can readily be seen that the load formula derived by Martin does not predict effective lubricant film thicknesses which are significant compared with the surface irregularities in most contacts.

Of the two important extensions to the classical hydrodynamic theory which have to be included in an analysis of highly loaded contacts, the effect of *elastic distortion* was the first to be considered. Peppler (1936, 1938) was concerned with the maximum oil film pressure which could occur in a contact between gear teeth lubricated by a constant viscosity fluid. He concluded that the maximum oil film pressure could never exceed the corresponding maximum Hertzian contact pressure; a conclusion which is no longer tenable. Meldahl (1941) also examined the effect of high pressure on film shape and pressure distribution for a constant viscosity lubricant. He derived expressions for the surface displacement of a semi-infinite elastic solid subjected to an arbitrary surface loading, and by coupling these equations with the Reynolds equation he was able to determine a satisfactory solution to the problem. Unfortunately, as the rate of convergence was poor and the labour required considerable, Meldahl only produced one result. Although Meldahl's solution did not flatter the beneficial effects of elastic distortion, it did move in the right direction, and his simultaneous solution of the elastic and hydrodynamic equations presented a possible approach to the problem.

Neither Peppler's nor Meldahl's work suggested that elastic distortion alone could account for the large increase in predicted load carrying capacity required to support the argument for the existence of a continuous fluid film between gear teeth. The second potentially important extension of lubrication theory was considered by Gatcombe (1945) when he examined theoretically the influence of the *viscosity–pressure* characteristics of a lubricant on film formation. For a particular viscosity–pressure relationship Gatcombe solved Reynolds' equation with rather arbitrary boundary conditions. Although a convenient equation for load carrying capacity was not developed, it was clear that the benefit to be derived from the effect of high pressures on lubricant viscosity alone was not big enough to allow the prediction of satisfactory fluid films between gear teeth. Gatcombe's analysis did however indicate that the predicted film thickness was increased, and in some of the examples quoted the order of magnitude of the predicted film thickness equalled representative surface irregularity measurements.

Hersey and Lowdenslager (1950) completed an investigation of the film thickness between rigid gear teeth lubricated by a fluid characterized by a parabolic viscosity–pressure relationship which was initiated by Karlson in 1926. In general terms the change in theoretical load capacity from the isoviscous prediction was found to be very similar to the improvement calculated by Gatcombe for an exponential relationship.

Several investigators took up the challenge at this stage, and Cameron (1952) and McEwen (1952) both extended Gat-

4 INTRODUCTION

combe's analysis by including a satisfactory cavitation boundary condition. McEwen considered a viscosity–pressure relationship of the form $\eta = \eta_0(1 + p/k)^n$ and he showed that, for values of n ranging from 6 to 11, the theoretical load capacity was increased above the Martin prediction by factors ranging from 2·8 to 2·4. At the same time Blok (1952) pointed out that for an exponential viscosity–pressure relationship there was a limiting film thickness at which the maximum pressure became infinite. For conditions represented by this mathematical restriction Blok showed that the load capacity was increased to approximately 2·3 times the corresponding Martin load; a figure consistent with McEwen's results. Blok (1950) had earlier presented an account of the influence of viscosity–pressure effects in a paper in which he considered a dimensional analysis of the problem.

Dörr (1954) re-examined the problem of elastic contacts lubricated by an iso-viscous fluid considered earlier by Peppler and Meldahl. He developed an iterative method in which the pressure distribution at any stage was employed in the calculation of surface displacements, and the displacements then added to the initial shape of the contacting solids to produce a slightly different oil film shape. The new geometry of the oil film was then used to re-calculate the pressure distribution, and the process was repeated until the film shape and pressure curve exhibited an adequate similarity to the previous solution.

At a somewhat earlier stage some extremely valuable work had been carried out in Russia. Grubin (1949) examined the problem theoretically, and although he did not produce solutions which satisfied the elasticity and lubrication equation throughout the entire contact, his analysis of the inlet region proved to be particularly useful. By assuming that the surfaces of the bounding solids would adopt the shape produced by dry contact, Grubin was able to examine the generation of pressure in the inlet region and to determine the required separation of the solids within the Hertzian contact zone. The analysis allowed for the effect of pressure upon viscosity. The most valuable result of this approach was the derivation of an approximate film thickness equation for highly loaded elastic contacts. This equation at once predicted film thicknesses which were orders of magnitude greater than the corresponding predictions of the Martin theory and consistent with the formation of satisfactory fluid films in gear contacts. In addition to his analysis of the inlet region, Grubin discussed in qualitative terms the distribution of oil film pressure throughout the contact zone. One of his main conclusions was that the pressure curve would exhibit a rather spectacular second maximum near the outlet end of the Hertzian zone. Grubin's analysis produced an excellent account of the physical mechanism of elasto-hydrodynamic lubrication, and his work represented the first successful examination of the combined effects of high pressure on the lubricant and the solids forming the contact.

The characteristics of an elasto-hydrodynamic contact predicted by Grubin were confirmed by Petrusevich (1951) when he obtained solutions which simultaneously satisfied the governing elastic and hydrodynamic equations. Although the computational difficulties were considerable, Petrusevich successfully obtained solutions for three different speeds. The three main features of these solutions, which are now confirmed as general characteristics of highly loaded lubricated contacts, are an almost parallel oil film in the contact zone with a local restriction near the outlet, a near Hertzian pressure curve over most of the zone and a very local second pressure maximum of considerable height near the outlet end of the zone.

Shortly after the Russian work, Poritsky (1952) reported an attempt to find a pressure distribution which satisfied the conditions in a lubricated contact. The approach was somewhat different from Petrusevich's and though no complete solutions were obtained the analysis is worthy of study.

For two cylinders Lewicki (1954) proposed a contact geometry consisting of two inclined Hertzian flats. Since the deformation of the elastic cylinders had been specified, the analysis was able to follow the conventional hydrodynamic lubrication procedure. A lubricant of constant density and viscosity was assumed. The model was in fact too simple, and the characteristics of an elasto-hydrodynamic contact which were being uncovered elsewhere did not emerge from the analysis.

Lewicki (1955) later described an experimental investigation of the thickness of lubricating films between cylindrical rollers. Two electrical methods, namely oil film resistance and capacitance, were employed, but only the capacitance measurements were thought to give an accurate measure of the effective separation of the solids. Oil film thicknesses of the order of 1μm (40 μin.) were recorded and the effective lubricant viscosity was found to be more closely related to the cylinder temperatures than to the oil bath temperature.

Weber and Saalfeld (1954) obtained an interesting closed solution to the elasto-hydrodynamic problem which considered both constant and pressure dependent viscosity. The solution was, however, limited to small deformations and it could not distinguish between the near Hertzian solutions which occur in most real contacts.

A number of solutions covering a range of conditions similar to that considered by Weber and Saalfeld, but also including the effect of temperature changes within the lubricant, have been presented by Hashimoto (1964). Hashimoto (1963) also developed a method for obtaining the oil film thickness from capacitance measurements.

Blok† set up a useful survey diagram of the currently available theoretical and experimental film thickness values which was also published by Peppler (1957). Blok (1959) later brought this diagram up to date by including the numerous theoretical results which became available between 1953 and 1959.

So far our account of the history of elasto-hydrodynamic lubrication has been mainly concerned with the development of the theory of the subject. The reason for this is that reliable quantitative experimental information about lubricating films in highly loaded elastic contacts did not become available until the late nineteen-fifties. Before this time the performance of *gears* and *disk machines* was taken as an indirect indication of

† Private communication Prof. H.Blok dated 16 July 1953.

the existence of fluid films in such contacts. The disk machines were built to simulate gear tooth contact, and they were used primarily to test the suitability of metals and lubricants for gear operating conditions.

A revolution in disk machine experiments was initiated by Crook (1958) when he reported the direct measurement of oil film thickness by *capacitance* and *oil flow* methods. Crook found that at low loads the thickness of the oil film was inversely proportional to load and proportional to speed as predicted by Martin's theory for rigid cylinders lubricated by an isoviscous fluid. At higher loads, which are more representative of the operating conditions in gears, the film thickness in pure rolling was found to be almost independent of the load; a result predicted by Grubin's film thickness formula. Furthermore, the measured film thickness at high loads was found to be considerably greater than the theoretical film thickness predicted by the Martin theory, and the typical value of $1 \mu m$ (40 μin.) quoted by Crook was consistent with the idea that a continuous oil film may exist between gear teeth. Crook (1961 a, b) later extended his investigation by considering the influence of viscosity and speed on film thickness. One of his major conclusions was that the viscosity of the lubricant at the surface temperature of the disks was of the greatest importatance in the determination of film thickness. Recently Crook (1963) has described measurements of friction and effective viscosity. The conclusion from this work is that rolling friction under elasto-hydrodynamic conditions is independent of load and proportional to film thickness. Measurements of effective viscosity in the contact led Crook to suggest that the visco-elastic behaviour of the lubricant may be important. This work is discussed in some detail in Chapters 9 and 10.

Other attempts to measure oil film thickness in highly loaded contacts were reported during the period covered by Crook's experiments. MacConochie and Cameron (1960) recorded the presence of fluid films between gear teeth by means of a *voltage discharge technique*. El-Sisi and Shawki (1960 a, b) also reported the development of an electrical resistance method for the measurement of film thickness. Unfortunately the method is inconvenient when applied to conventional lubricating oils, and of all the electrical methods so far attempted, capacitance, as employed by Crook appears to be the most reliable.

An alternative experimental approach was described by Sibley and Orcutt (1961) when they presented film thickness measurements based upon an *X-ray transmission technique*. Results were obtained for white mineral oil, diester-base and silicone lubricants over a wide range of viscosities, speeds and loads. In addition the transverse profiles of the elastically deformed solids in the vicinity of the contact were recorded. The film thicknesses recorded by Sibley and Orcutt are in overall agreement with Crook's measurements and current elasto-hydrodynamic theory. It is clear that the experimental work of the late nineteen-fifties provided valuable data on the lubrication of highly loaded contacts, and we now return to the development of elasto-hydrodynamic theory during this era.

Korovchinskii (1960) examined the general problem of lubrication for deformable bodies and he presented the basic elasticity and lubrication equations together with appropriate boundary conditions. His discussion of the simplest sufficiently accurate procedure for solving the elasto-hydrodynamic problem considered viscous (incompressible) and plastic (non work-hardening) lubricants. In addition the equations governing the normal approach of two elastic bodies separated by a lubricant were established. Kodnir (1960) considered the load carrying capacity of numerous oil film profiles for constant and pressure-dependent viscosity lubricants. In this paper Kodnir appreciated the essential shape of elasto-hydrodynamic oil films and some interesting experiments were described. The experimental aspect of the work is discussed in Chapter 8.

A new approach to elasto-hydrodynamic theory was presented by Dowson and Higginson (1959). Even for the relatively simple case of a constant viscosity fluid, the straightforward iterative processes employed by Meldahl and Dörr are tedious and only slowly convergent. By introducing a solution of the inverse hydrodynamic lubrication problem, Dowson and Higginson were able to overcome this difficulty and to obtain satisfactory solutions of the elastic and hydrodynamic equations after a small number of cycles. This process which is described in detail in Chapter 6, was first applied to the problem of a highly loaded contact between bronze disks lubricated by a mineral oil. The viscosity–pressure relationship for an actual lubricant was employed in the calculations. Solutions were obtained for a range of loads at a single speed, and although most of the characteristics of the solutions were consistent with Petrusevish's results, a notable difference was the absence of the high second pressure peak. This discrepancy was explained when Dowson and Higginson (1960) reported further solutions which covered a range of loads, speeds and material properties. It was found that the existence and form of the second pressure peak was a function of all these variables, and the initial calculations were related to conditions which were not conducive to the formation of a second pressure peak. In particular the value of a dimensionless materials parameter formed by the product of the exponential viscosity–pressure coefficient for the lubricant and the effective elastic modulus for the solids was shown to be influential in determining the distribution of pressure in a highly loaded contact.

Details of the pressure curve were not, however, of prime importance at this stage. The posibility of hydrodnamic lubrication clearly depends upon the formation of a continuous lubricant film which has an effective thickness at least as big as the surface irregularities on the opposing solids. Dowson and Higginson (1961) analysed their solutions and found that a convenient dimensionless formula for minimum film thickness could be written in terms of the load, speed and material parameters. The close agreement between the theoretical minimum film thickness predictions and the experimental results obtained by Crook and Sibley demonstrated that the gap between theory and experiment had been largely closed. For pure rolling, which approximates to the hypothetical isothermal conditions assumed in the theory, the minimum film thickness in highly loaded contacts could now be calculated with some confidence.

The influence of speed and lubricant compressibility on a theoretical solution to the elasto-hydrodynamic problem was fully considered by Dowson, Higginson and Whitaker (1962) when they presented a survey of isothermal solutions. Speed was shown to be the most important variable in the problem and the inclusion of lubricant compressibility in the theory was found to have an appreciable influence on pressure distribution but little effect on minimum film thickness.

A survey of the isothermal solutions for film thickness which covered the full load range from lightly loaded (Martin) conditions to very highly loaded (elasto-hydrodynamic) conditions was presented by Dowson and Whitaker (1964). In this paper computing methods were also discussed in some detail.

In an ambitious analysis Sternlicht, Lewis and Flynn (1961) considered the distribution of pressure and temperature in highly loaded contacts. The introduction of an energy equation considerably increased the computational effort required, but by writing the equations in finite difference form and employing a digital computer a successful iterative process was established. Few details of the results were included in this paper but some of the conclusions, particularly with respect to the influence of lubricant properties on fatigue life, are of general interest.

The analysis of thermal effects in contacts exhibiting mixed rolling and sliding has been extended by Cheng and Sternlicht (1964). These authors considered the difficult mathematical problem presented by the requirement for a solution of the Reynolds, elasticity, energy and heat transfer equations for a cylindrical contact. The results indicated that the basic features of the elasto-hydrodynamic contact indicated by isothermal theory were also evident in solutions for sliding conditions. In particular the sharp secondary pressure peak predicted for a Newtonian fluid in pure rolling conditions was found to persist, and even grow, when some sliding was introduced.

Another feature of the Cheng and Sternlicht solutions which is of considerable practical importance is that the calculated film thickness is not appreciably influenced by the oil film temperatures generated in sliding contacts. The isothermal film thickness formula gives good approximations to the measured film thickness if the lubricant viscosity corresponding to the temperature at inlet to the film is considered.

The new understanding of highly loaded lubricated contacts has called for a re-examination of the mechanism of fatigue failure. The well-known type of failure known as *pitting* has been investigated by Dawson (1961). The role of the lubricant was clearly indicated and in a subsequent paper Dawson (1962) found that the ratio of the surface roughness to the oil film thickness had a profound effect on the pitting behaviour of lubricated rolling contacts. The Hertzian ellipse of dry contact has been employed in the past as the distribution of surface stress associated with highly loaded contacts. The elasto-hydrodynamic theory now available shows that this distribution of pressure may be considerably modified if a lubricant is present. The sub-surface stresses corresponding to typical elasto-hydrodynamic pressure distributions have been computed by Dowson, Higginson and Whitaker (1963).

Archard, Gair and Hirst (1961) confirmed the overall shape of the oil film and the distribution of pressure predicted earlier for an incompressible fluid. Although fine detail was dispensed with in some regions of the pressure zone, several interesting features of highly loaded contacts emerged from this work. Bell (1961) contributed an interesting examination of the effects of non-Newtonian behaviour when he considered the lubrication of rolling surfaces by a Ree–Eyring fluid. He concluded that at high rates of shear the influence of velocity on film thickness should diminish, whereas the influence of load should increase. The influence of non-Newtonian behaviour of the lubricant in rolling contacts has also been studied by Milne (1957), Tanner (1960) and Burton (1960).

The analytical solutions so far described have all been related to rolling or sliding contacts in the steady state. It is as well to note here that elasto-hydrodynamic effects can also occur during the normal approach of two solids separated by a fluid. Christensen (1962) theoretically examined the normal approach problem in some detail and he found that the solids could be elastically indented by fluid film pressures which considerably exceeded the corresponding Hertzian stresses. As the deformation proceeds, the region of minimum film thickness moves away from the line of centres to form a ring which tends to restrict the radial flow of the lubricant. The fluid contained within the indented region cushions the approach of the solids, and Christensen showed that the fluid pressures ultimately adopt the Hertzian distribution of normal surface stress in dry contact. It is interesting to note that the dimensionless materials parameter discussed earlier has an important influence on pressure distribution in normal approach as well as in rolling and sliding.

Once the existence of a coherent fluid film in some highly loaded contacts had been established, the coefficient of friction became the subject of several investigations. Misharin (1958) found that the coefficient of friction between two rollers obeyed the laws of elasto-hydrodynamic theory as developed by Petrusevich. He found that the friction coefficient increased as the operating temperature was raised and that it decreased slightly with an increase in either sliding or rolling velocity.

Smith (1959) measured the friction force in a sliding contact between a sphere and a plane. He concluded from the wear scars that, under some conditions, most of the contact operated hydrodynamically, and the measurements of friction forces under these conditions suggested that the coefficient of friction decreased as the sliding speed increased. In the same paper Smith described a rolling and sliding experiment in which a cylinder was driven against a spherical surface which rotated about an axis slightly skewed in relation to the axis of the cylinder. From the experimental force components Smith concluded that the lubricant in the contact zone sheared like a plastic solid along a thin band which represented a small proportion of the film thickness. Smith (1962) later investigated the effect of temperature upon friction forces and he recorded a decrease in coefficient of friction with increasing temperature; a trend which conflicts with Misharin's results. Although the geometry of the contacts employed by Misharin and Smith are quite different, and the experiments are in fact measuring different things, this conflict is so fundamental that further experimental work is required. In a paper dealing with rolling contact lubrication and wear research, Smith (1961) distinguishes between six types of contact conditions. Once a coherent fluid film has formed the linear relationship between coefficient of friction and sliding speed suggests that the conventional Newtonian characteristics of the lubricant predominate. At higher sliding speeds non-Newtonian effects are in evidence and the subsequent fall in the value of the friction coefficient is attributed to internal heating of the fluid.

An interesting paper by Archard and Kirk (1961) demonstrated that fluid film lubrication can also occur in some highly loaded point contacts. Hitherto it had been considered that only boundary lubrication could occur under these extreme conditions. The paper draws attention to the development of an elasto-hydrodynamic contact possessing many of the features described earlier for nominal line contacts.

Several model experiments in elasto-hydrodynamic lubrication have been reported recently. Bell (1961) observed the deformation of a low elastic modulus spherical cap by a light absorption technique. The distribution of oil film pressure between a bronze drum and a synthetic rubber block was measured by Higginson (1962). In both these experiments substantial elastic deformation is achieved with relatively low fluid pressures. The behaviour of lubricated Perspex contacts has been discussed by Kirk (1962) in a note in which the measurement of film thickness by direct observation of white light fringes is described.

The distribution of pressure in a highly loaded lubricated contact between bronze surfaces was recorded by Dowson and Longfield (1963). The small dimensions of the Hertzian zone in typical engineering contacts prohibits the measurement of pressure by conventional means. Dowson and Longfield overcame this difficulty by producing a large contact zone between conforming surfaces in an unconventional disk machine. The measured pressures confirmed the overall theoretical predictions for an infinitely wide contact of the same proportions produced earlier by Dowson and Higginson (1959).

Most of the early interest in elasto-hydrodynamics has been justifiably focussed on the thickness of the effective lubricating films. Now that adequate equations for the calculation of film thickness have been developed for representative rolling contacts, other aspects of the problem such as the effect of sliding, the distribution of pressure in the fluid and stresses in the solids, the frictional characteristics of lubricated contacts and the rheological properties of lubricants under contact conditions are attracting more attention. A good deal is now known about the behaviour of idealized contacts and it should be possible to apply this knowledge to an analysis of many real contacts. A first step in this direction was taken by Dowson and Higginson (1963) when they carried out an elasto-hydrodynamic analysis of roller bearings.

A fundamental feature of the analysis of real contacts is the representation by *equivalent cylinders*. This device, which facilitates mathematical analysis and experimental investigation and which will be referred to throughout this book, will now be described.

Representation of Contacts by Cylinders

Many contacts between machine components can be represented by cylinders which provide good geometrical agreement with the profile of the undeformed solids in the immediate vicinity of the contact. The geometrical errors at some distance from the contact are of little importance. Two well-known examples will be considered, but other contacts can be analysed in a similar way.

For roller bearings the solids are already cylindrical as shown in Fig. 1.1. On the inner race or track the contact is formed by two convex cylinders of radii r and R_1, and on the outer race the contact is between the roller of radius r and the concave surface of radius $(R_1 + 2r)$. For involute gears it can readily be shown (see, for example, Merritt, 1942) that the contact at a distance s from the pitch point can be represented by two cylinders of radii $(R_{1,2} \sin \psi \pm s)$ rotating with the angular velocities of the wheels. In this expression R represents the pitch

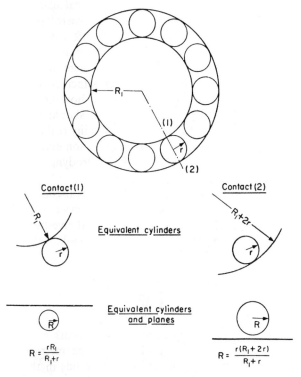

FIG. 1.1. Equivalent cylinders for cylindrical roller bearing.

radius of the wheels and ψ is the pressure angle. The geometry of an involute gear contact is shown in Fig. 1.2. This form of representation explains the use of disk machines to simulate gear tooth contacts and facilitate measurements of force components and film thicknesses. The practical form of disk machines will be discussed in Chapters 8 and 9.

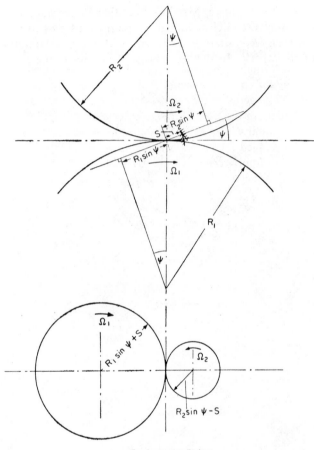

Equivalent cylinders

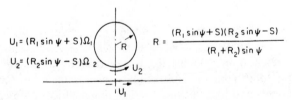

$$U_1 = (R_1 \sin \psi + S)\Omega_1$$

$$U_2 = (R_2 \sin \psi - S)\Omega_2$$

$$R = \frac{(R_1 \sin\psi + S)(R_2 \sin\psi - S)}{(R_1 + R_2)\sin\psi}$$

FIG. 1.2. Equivalent cylinders for involute gears.

Equivalent Cylinders

From the point of view of a mathematical analysis the contact between two cylinders as shown in Fig. 1.3(a) can be adequately described by an equivalent cylinder near a plane as shown in Fig. 1.3(b). The geometrical requirement is that the separation of the cylinders in the initial and equivalent contact should be the same at equal values of x. This simple equivalence can be adequately satisfied in the important region of small x, but it falls down as x approaches the radii of the cylinders. The radius of the equivalent cylinder is determined as follows.

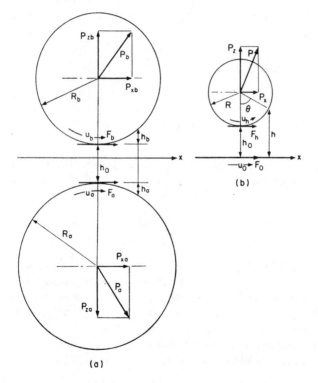

Fig. 1.3. Equivalent cylinders.

From Fig. 1.3(a),

$$h = h_0 + h_a + h_b$$

$$h \approx h_0 + \frac{x^2}{2R_a} + \frac{x^2}{2R_b}$$

$$h \approx h_0 + \frac{x^2}{2} \left(\frac{1}{R_a} + \frac{1}{R_b} \right)$$

For the equivalent cylinder,

$$h \approx h_0 + \frac{x^2}{2R}$$

Hence the separation of the solids at any given value of x will be equal if,

$$\frac{1}{R} = \frac{1}{R_a} + \frac{1}{R_b}$$

The radius of the equivalent cylinder is then,

$$R = \frac{R_a R_b}{R_a + R_b}$$

If the centres of the cylinders lie on the same side of the common tangent at the contact point and $R_a > R_b$ the radius of the equivalent cylinder takes the form,

$$R = \frac{R_a R_b}{R_a - R_b}$$

From the lubrication point of view the representation of a contact by an equivalent cylinder near a plane is adequate when pressure generation is considered, but care must be exercised in relating the force components on the original cylinders to the force components on the equivalent cylinder.

The normal force components along the line of centres shown in Fig. 1.3 are directly equivalent since, by definition,

$$P_{za} = P_{zb} = P_z = \int p \, dx$$

The normal force components in the direction of sliding are defined as,

$$P_{xa} = -\int p \, dh_a = -\frac{1}{R_a} \int px \, dx$$

$$P_{xb} = -\int p \, dh_b = -\frac{1}{R_b} \int px \, dx$$

and

$$P_x = -\int p \, dh = -\frac{1}{R} \int px \, dx$$

Hence,

$$P_{xa} = \frac{R}{R_a} P_x$$

and

$$P_{xb} = \frac{R}{R_b} P_x$$

For the friction force components it can also be seen that,

$$F_a = F_0 = \int \tau_0 \, dx$$

$$F_b = F_h = \int \tau_h \, dx$$

where $\tau_{0,h}$ represents the tangential surface stresses acting on the solids.

CHAPTER 2

LUBRICATION EQUATIONS

The Reynolds Equation

THE equation which governs the generation of pressure in lubricating films is known as the *Reynolds equation*. Reynolds (1886) first derived the equation, and it forms the foundation of hydrodynamic lubrication analysis. The relevant form of the equation will now be derived.

The effective radius of curvature of bearing components is generally very large compared with the film thickness. This observation enables the analysis to consider an equivalent curved surface near a plane; all effects due to curvature of the fluid film being neglected. A representative lubricating film geometry is shown in Fig. 2.1. It will be assumed that the lubricant behaves like a Newtonian fluid; an assumption which implies that the viscous shear stress is at all times proportional to the rate of shear. There is some evidence of non-Newtonian behaviour in elasto-hydrodynamic films, particularly where friction force measurements are concerned, but the theoretical analysis will be limited to Newtonian fluids.

The Reynolds equation is derived by applying the basic equations of motion and continuity to the lubricant. The full equations of motion for a Newtonian fluid in cartesian coordinates have been derived, for example, by Pai (1956). The equations can be written in the following form,

$$\varrho \, \frac{du}{dt} = \varrho X - \frac{\partial p}{\partial x} + \frac{2}{3} \frac{\partial}{\partial x} \, \eta \left(\frac{\partial u}{\partial x} - \frac{\partial w}{\partial z} \right)$$

$$+ \frac{2}{3} \frac{\partial}{\partial x} \eta \left(\frac{\partial u}{\partial x} - \frac{\partial v}{\partial y} \right) + \frac{\partial}{\partial y} \eta \left(\frac{\partial u}{\partial y} + \frac{\partial v}{\partial x} \right)$$

$$+ \frac{\partial}{\partial z} \eta \left(\frac{\partial w}{\partial x} + \frac{\partial u}{\partial z} \right)$$

$$\varrho \frac{dv}{dt} = \varrho Y - \frac{\partial p}{\partial y} + \frac{2}{3} \frac{\partial}{\partial y} \eta \left(\frac{\partial v}{\partial y} - \frac{\partial u}{\partial x} \right)$$

$$+ \frac{2}{3} \frac{\partial}{\partial y} \eta \left(\frac{\partial v}{\partial y} - \frac{\partial w}{\partial z} \right) + \frac{\partial}{\partial z} \eta \left(\frac{\partial v}{\partial z} + \frac{\partial w}{\partial y} \right)$$

$$+ \frac{\partial}{\partial x} \eta \left(\frac{\partial v}{\partial x} + \frac{\partial u}{\partial y} \right)$$

$$\varrho \frac{dw}{dt} = \varrho Z - \frac{\partial p}{\partial z} + \frac{2}{3} \frac{\partial}{\partial z} \eta \left(\frac{\partial w}{\partial z} - \frac{\partial u}{\partial x} \right)$$

$$+ \frac{2}{3} \frac{\partial}{\partial z} \eta \left(\frac{\partial w}{\partial z} - \frac{\partial v}{\partial y} \right) + \frac{\partial}{\partial x} \eta \left(\frac{\partial w}{\partial x} + \frac{\partial u}{\partial z} \right)$$

$$+ \frac{\partial}{\partial y} \eta \left(\frac{\partial w}{\partial y} + \frac{\partial v}{\partial z} \right)$$

The terms on the left-hand side represent inertia effects and on the right-hand side are the body force, pressure and viscous terms in that order.

The equation of continuity representing conservation of mass is,

$$\frac{\partial \varrho}{\partial t} + \frac{\partial (\varrho u)}{\partial x} + \frac{\partial (\varrho v)}{\partial y} + \frac{\partial (\varrho w)}{\partial z} = 0 \qquad (2.2)$$

For representative lubricating films, the inertia and body forces can be shown to be negligible compared with the viscous and pressure forces. If the inertia and body force terms are

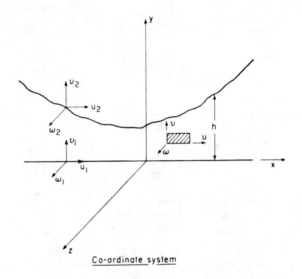

Co-ordinate system

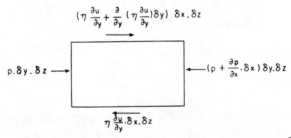

[Surface forces (x direction) acting on an element of fluid]

For equilibrium in x direction;— $\dfrac{\partial p}{\partial x} = \dfrac{\partial}{\partial y}\, \eta\,(\dfrac{\partial u}{\partial y})$

FIG. 2.1. Coordinate system and surface forces acting on an element of fluid.

neglected, the reduced equations of motion imply that the pressure and viscous forces acting on the fluid are in equilibrium. When the first equation of motion is reduced in this way it takes the form:

$$\frac{\partial p}{\partial x} = \frac{2}{3} \frac{\partial}{\partial x} \eta \left(\frac{\partial u}{\partial x} - \frac{\partial w}{\partial z} \right) + \frac{2}{3} \frac{\partial}{\partial x} \eta \left(\frac{\partial u}{\partial x} - \frac{\partial v}{\partial y} \right)$$

$$+ \frac{\partial}{\partial y} \eta \left(\frac{\partial u}{\partial y} + \frac{\partial v}{\partial x} \right) + \frac{\partial}{\partial z} \eta \left(\frac{\partial w}{\partial x} + \frac{\partial u}{\partial z} \right)$$

Similar expressions are obtained for the y- and z-directions. Owing to the minute thickness of the fluid film in relation to other dimensions in a lubricated contact, the derivates of the velocity components u and w with respect to y are large compared with all other velocity gradients. Furthermore, if l is a representative length of the contact or bearing, the pressure gradient across the film (i.e. in the y-direction), can be shown to be of order (h/l) times the pressure gradients along the film. Since $h \ll l$ the variation of pressure across the film is normally quite insignificant. These observations permit the second equation of motion to be neglected. The remaining equations of motion become,

$$\left. \begin{array}{l} \dfrac{\partial p}{\partial x} = \dfrac{\partial}{\partial y} \eta \left(\dfrac{\partial u}{\partial y} \right) \\[3mm] \dfrac{\partial p}{\partial z} = \dfrac{\partial}{\partial y} \eta \left(\dfrac{\partial w}{\partial y} \right) \end{array} \right\} \tag{2.3}$$

With the restrictions employed above, the equilibrium eqns. (2.3) can be derived directly from a balance of the surface forces acting on a fluid element as shown in Fig. 2.1. It should be noted that the analysis has not been restricted to an isoviscous fluid. Furthermore, since an equation of state has not yet been introduced, the equations apply to compressible and incompressible fluids.

Equations (2.3) can be integrated directly with respect to y to yield the velocity gradients,

$$\left.\begin{aligned}
\frac{\partial u}{\partial y} &= \frac{y}{\eta}\frac{\partial p}{\partial x} + \frac{A(x, z)}{\eta} \\[2mm]
\frac{\partial w}{\partial y} &= \frac{y}{\eta}\frac{\partial p}{\partial z} + \frac{B(x, z)}{\eta}
\end{aligned}\right\} \tag{2.4}$$

General expressions for the velocity components are obtained when these equations are integrated again with respect to y.

$$u = \frac{\partial p}{\partial x}\int \frac{y}{\eta}\,\mathrm{d}y + A(x, z)\int \frac{\mathrm{d}y}{\eta} + C(x, z)$$

$$w = \frac{\partial p}{\partial z}\int \frac{y}{\eta}\,\mathrm{d}y + B(x, z)\int \frac{\mathrm{d}y}{\eta} + D(x, z)$$

At this stage it will be assumed that the viscosity is a function of x and z only. If the viscosity varies across the film the above integrals have to be fully considered. A general derivation of the Reynolds equation which takes account of fluid property variations along and across the film, and which discusses in detail the assumptions made earlier has been presented by Dowson (1962).

The boundary values for velocity are,

$$y = 0, \quad u = u_1, \quad w = w_1$$

$$y = h, \quad u = u_2, \quad w = w_2$$

With these values and the assumption that the viscosity is independent of y the velocity components become

$$\left.\begin{aligned}
u &= \left(1 - \frac{y}{h}\right)u_1 + \frac{y}{h}u_2 - \frac{y(h - y)}{2\eta}\frac{\partial p}{\partial x} \\[2mm]
w &= \left(1 - \frac{y}{h}\right)w_1 + \frac{y}{h}w_2 - \frac{y(h - y)}{2\eta}\frac{\partial p}{\partial z}
\end{aligned}\right\} \tag{2.5}$$

The Reynolds equation is formed by introducing these expressions into the continuity eqn. (2.2) and integrating with respect to y. With the limits $y = 0, h$ the integral for the steady state becomes,

$$\int_0^h \frac{\partial}{\partial x} (\varrho u) \, dy + \int_0^h \frac{\partial}{\partial z} (\varrho w) \, dy + \left[\varrho v \right]_0^h = 0$$

This equation can be expanded according to the general result,

$$\int_{h_1}^{h_2} \frac{\partial}{\partial x} f(x, y, z) \, dy = \frac{\partial}{\partial x} \int_{h_1}^{h_2} f(x, y, z) \, dy - f(x, h_2, z) \frac{\partial h_2}{\partial x}$$

$$+ f(x, h_1, z) \frac{\partial h_1}{\partial x}$$

to give,

$$\frac{\partial}{\partial x} \int_0^h (\varrho u) \, dy + \frac{\partial}{\partial z} \int_0^h (\varrho w) \, dy - (\varrho u)_2 \frac{\partial h}{\partial x} - (\varrho w)_2 \frac{\partial h}{\partial z}$$

$$+ \left[\varrho v \right]_0^h = 0$$

The density will not normally vary appreciably across the film, and when this is accepted and the velocity relationships (2.5) are introduced, the following equation is generated.

$$\frac{\partial}{\partial x} \left(\frac{\varrho h^3}{12 \eta} \frac{\partial p}{\partial x} \right) + \frac{\partial}{\partial z} \left(\frac{\varrho h^3}{12 \eta} \frac{\partial p}{\partial z} \right)$$

$$= \frac{\partial}{\partial x} \left(\frac{\varrho h (u_1 + u_2)}{2} \right) + \frac{\partial}{\partial z} \left(\frac{\varrho h (w_1 + w_2)}{2} \right)$$

$$- \varrho u_2 \frac{\partial h}{\partial x} - \varrho w_2 \frac{\partial h}{\partial z} + \varrho(v_2 - v_1)$$

$$(2.6)$$

This is the general form of the *Reynolds equation* within the range of conditions now being discussed. The values to be attributed to the boundary velocities need to be carefully defined before the right-hand side is further reduced.

Interpretation of Boundary Velocities

The specification of boundary velocities u_1, v_1, w_1, for the plane surface does not present any difficulty. In general the surface velocities of the upper bearing component need to be related to the translation of the component parallel to the co-ordinate axes and the rotation of the component about its own centre. In subsequent chapters we shall be concerned with boundary velocities confined to the following values.

$$u_1 = u_1, \quad v_1 = 0, \quad w_1 = 0$$

$$u_2 = u_2, \quad v_2 \approx u_2 \frac{\partial h}{\partial x}, \quad w_2 = 0$$

where u_1, u_2 are the surface velocities of the two bearing components in the x-direction.

For these conditions the Reynolds equation becomes,

$$\frac{\partial}{\partial x}\left(\frac{\varrho h^3}{12\eta}\frac{\partial p}{\partial x}\right) + \frac{\partial}{\partial z}\left(\frac{\varrho h^3}{12\eta}\frac{\partial p}{\partial z}\right) = \frac{\partial}{\partial x}(\varrho u h) \qquad (2.7)$$

where

$$u = \frac{u_1 + u_2}{2}$$

Again it should be emphasized that this equation allows for variation of the fluid property values in the x- and z-directions. The equation also permits the bearing surfaces to be of finite length in the z-direction. Side-leakage, or flow in the z-direction, is associated with the second term in eqn. (2.7). If the pressure in the lubricant has to be considered as a function of x

and z, the solution of (2.7) can rarely be achieved analytically. Approximate numerical solutions are therefore sought and the process is usually laborious. In many conventional lubrication problems, side-leakage can be neglected, and this often leads to analytical solutions. It will be argued later that side-leakage is likely to be of less importance in elasto-hydrodynamic analysis than in conventional lubrication problems.

If side-leakage is neglected, eqn. (2.7) reduces to

$$\frac{\mathrm{d}}{\mathrm{d}x}\left(\frac{\varrho h^3}{12\eta}\frac{\mathrm{d}p}{\mathrm{d}x}\right) = \frac{\mathrm{d}}{\mathrm{d}x}(\varrho uh) \qquad (2.8)$$

This equation can be integrated with respect to x to yield the familiar integrated form of the Reynolds equation,

$$\frac{\mathrm{d}p}{\mathrm{d}x} = 12\eta u\left[\frac{\varrho h - (\varrho h)_m}{\varrho h^3}\right] \qquad (2.9)$$

where the suffix m refers to conditions at the point of maximum pressure. If the lubricant is incompressible, eqn. (2.9) reduces further to the form,

$$\frac{\mathrm{d}p}{\mathrm{d}x} = 12\eta u\left[\frac{h - h_m}{h^3}\right] \qquad (2.10)$$

The normal hydrodynamic lubrication problem presents a known film shape and requires the determination of a pressure curve. In the absence of side-leakage, eqns. (2.9) or (2.10) can be integrated to yield the pressure distribution. This standard procedure will be described in detail for a particular geometry in the next chapter.

In elasto-hydrodynamic analysis it has been found useful to solve the inverse problem; that is to determine the shape of the lubricant film which will generate a given pressure distribution. The processes involved in a solution of the inverse hydrodynamic problem are described in detail in Chapter 6.

The Energy Equation

The equation used to determine the distribution of temperature within the fluid is a mathematical statement of the principle of energy conservation. Pai (1956) has presented a derivation of the energy equation for a fluid, and the full equation can be written as,

$$\varrho \frac{\mathrm{d}E}{\mathrm{d}t} = \left[\frac{\partial}{\partial x} \left(k \frac{\partial \theta}{\partial x} \right) + \frac{\partial}{\partial y} \left(k \frac{\partial \theta}{\partial y} \right) + \frac{\partial}{\partial z} \left(k \frac{\partial \theta}{\partial z} \right) \right]$$

convection   conduction

$$- p \left(\frac{\partial u}{\partial x} + \frac{\partial v}{\partial y} + \frac{\partial w}{\partial z} \right) + \varphi \qquad (2.11)$$

adiabatic   viscous
compression   dissipation

where

$$\varphi = \eta \left[\left(\frac{\partial u}{\partial z} \right)^2 + \left(\frac{\partial u}{\partial y} \right)^2 + \left(\frac{\partial v}{\partial x} \right)^2 + \left(\frac{\partial v}{\partial z} \right)^2 + \left(\frac{\partial w}{\partial x} \right)^2 \right.$$

$$+ \left(\frac{\partial w}{\partial y} \right)^2 + 2 \left(\frac{\partial u}{\partial y} \frac{\partial v}{\partial x} + \frac{\partial v}{\partial z} \frac{\partial w}{\partial y} + \frac{\partial w}{\partial x} \frac{\partial u}{\partial z} \right)$$

$$+ \frac{4}{3} \left\{ \frac{\partial u}{\partial x} \left(\frac{\partial u}{\partial x} - \frac{\partial v}{\partial y} \right) + \frac{\partial v}{\partial y} \left(\frac{\partial v}{\partial y} - \frac{\partial w}{\partial z} \right) \right.$$

$$\left. \left. + \frac{\partial w}{\partial z} \left(\frac{\partial w}{\partial z} - \frac{\partial u}{\partial x} \right) \right\} \right] \qquad (2.12)$$

The very small value of the ratio h/l in film lubricated bearings and contacts has already been mentioned in connection with the Reynolds equation. This general geometrical consideration normally allows the convection term to be dropped from the energy equation in lubrication analysis; the entry length in which the convection of heat in the fluid is significant compared with other modes of heat transfer being small compared with the bearing or contact length. Likewise the rate at which heat can be conducted along the film (i.e. in the x- and z-directions) is small compared with the rate of conduction to the bearing surfaces. The significant terms in the viscous dissipation expression are seen to be those involving differentials of u and w in the y-direction, and the reduced energy equation for lubricating films thus becomes,

$$\frac{\partial}{\partial y}\left(k\,\frac{\partial\theta}{\partial y}\right) - p\left(\frac{\partial u}{\partial x} + \frac{\partial v}{\partial y} + \frac{\partial w}{\partial z}\right)$$
$$+ \eta\left\{\left(\frac{\partial u}{\partial y}\right)^2 + \left(\frac{\partial w}{\partial y}\right)^2\right\} = 0 \qquad (2.13)$$

If the lubricant is considered to be an incompressible fluid the adiabatic compression term in eqn. (2.13) is zero. It should be noted, however, that this assumption is not likely to be valid for realistic elasto-hydrodynamic contacts. Furthermore, the thermal conductivity of liquid lubricants can often be treated as a constant in lubrication problems, and if both these assumptions are acceptable the energy equation adopts the following simple form,

$$k\,\frac{\partial^2\theta}{\partial y^2} + \eta\left\{\left(\frac{\partial u}{\partial y}\right)^2 + \left(\frac{\partial w}{\partial y}\right)^2\right\} = 0 \qquad (2.14)$$

This equation represents a balance between the rate of heat production within the film by viscous action and the rate of heat conduction from the film to the boundary solids.

The theoretical analysis of elasto-hydrodynamic contacts presented in subsequent chapters will assume isothermal conditions, and hence the energy equation will not be encountered. It will be shown that this assumption appears to be justified in the case of pure rolling, and as far as film thickness prediction is concerned it may also be acceptable for sliding contacts if an appropriate contact temperature is selected. The friction forces encountered are of course strongly dependent upon lubricant viscosity and hence temperature, and the energy equation will be introduced in Chapter 10 when the experimental results dealing with friction forces are discussed.

CHAPTER 3

LUBRICATION OF RIGID CYLINDERS

It has been shown in Chapter 1 that many highly loaded machine contacts can be represented by cylinders. Furthermore, in the important region near to the contact, the geometry can be represented by an equivalent cylinder near a plane. In the notation of Fig. 1.3 the separation between two circular cylinders of radii R_a and R_b at a distance x from the line of centres can be written as,

$$h = h_0 + R_a \left(1 - \left[1 - \left(\frac{x}{R_a} \right)^2 \right]^{1/2} \right)$$
$$+ R_b \left(1 - \left[1 - \left(\frac{x}{R_b} \right)^2 \right]^{1/2} \right) \qquad (3.1)$$

where h_0 is the separation on the line of centres.

Equation (3.1) can be expanded to give,

$$h = h_0 + R_a \left(\frac{1}{2} \left(\frac{x}{R_a} \right)^2 + \frac{1}{8} \left(\frac{x}{R_a} \right)^4 + \frac{1}{16} \left(\frac{x}{R_a} \right)^6 + \cdots \right)$$
$$+ R_b \left(\frac{1}{2} \left(\frac{x}{R_b} \right)^2 + \frac{1}{8} \left(\frac{x}{R_b} \right)^4 + \frac{1}{16} \left(\frac{x}{R_b} \right)^6 + \cdots \right)$$
$$(3.2)$$

If x/R_a and x/R_b are both small compared with unity a good approximation to the separation is obtained by neglecting the fourth and higher powers in eqn. (3.2). This gives the parabolic representation employed in Chapter 1. The error involved in this representation is shown in Table 3.1, where values of $(h - h_0)/R$ for a *parabolic profile* of latus-rectum $2R$ and a *circular cylinder* of radius R are compared.

TABLE 3.1

$\dfrac{x}{R}$		0	0·1	0·2	0·4	0·6	0·8	1·0	2
$\left(\dfrac{h-h_o}{R}\right)$	circular cylinder	0	0·00501	0·0202	0·0835	0·20	0·40	1·0	—
	parabolic cylinder	0	0·00500	0·0200	0·0800	0·18	0·32	0·5	1·0

Although the parabolic approximation is not very good at values of $x/R_{a,b}$ approaching unity, the effect on solutions of the Reynolds equation is small. This will be seen from a comparison of the solutions for rigid circular and parabolic cylinders. A solution for the circular cylinder has been presented by Floberg (1961) and the parabolic cylinder has been analysed by Martin (1916) and Purday (1949).

Solution of the Reynolds Equation for a Rigid Circular Cylinder and Plane

The geometry and surface velocities are shown in Fig. 3.1. At this stage an isoviscous fluid will be considered and side-leakage will be neglected. The appropriate form of the integrated Reynolds equation is,

$$\frac{dp}{dx} = 12\eta u \left(\frac{h - h_m}{h^3} \right) \tag{2.10}$$

For the circular cylinder shown in Fig. 3.1a we can write,

$$x = R \sin \theta$$

$$h = h_0 + R - R \cos \theta$$

$$h = (h_0 + R)\left(1 - \frac{R}{h_0 + R} \cos \theta\right)$$

$$h = -\frac{R}{n}(1 + n \cos \theta)$$

where,

$$n = \frac{-\dfrac{R}{h_0}}{1 + \dfrac{R}{h_0}} = \frac{-s}{1 + s}$$

$$s = \frac{R}{h_0}$$

On expressing x and h in terms of R, n and θ, the Reynolds equation becomes

$$\frac{dp}{d\theta} = \frac{12\eta n^2 u}{R}\left[\frac{\cos \theta}{(1 + n \cos \theta)^2} + \frac{nh_m}{R}\frac{\cos \theta}{(1 + n \cos \theta)^3}\right] \quad (3.3)$$

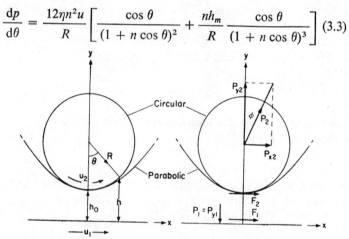

(a) Co-ordinates and velocities   (b) Forces

FIG. 3.1. Lubrication of a rigid cylinder and plane.

Now $R = [-n/(1 + n)] h_0$, and if the dimensionless pressure

$$\bar{p} = p \, \frac{h_0}{2\eta u}$$

is introduced, the general form of the pressure distribution becomes,

$$\bar{p} = -6r(1 + n) \left[\int \frac{\cos \theta}{(1 + n \cos \theta)^2} \, d\theta \right.$$

$$\left. + \frac{nh_m}{R} \int \frac{\cos \theta}{(1 + n \cos \theta)^3} \, d\theta + D \right] \qquad (3.4)$$

The integrals of equation (3.4) can be conveniently evaluated in terms of the Sommerfeld variable encountered in journal bearing analysis. With the Sommerfeld transformation defined by the equation,

$$1 + n \cos \theta = \frac{1 - n^2}{1 - n \cos \gamma}$$

the pressure distribution becomes,

$$\bar{p} = -6n(1 + n) \left[F_1(n, \gamma) + \frac{nh_m}{R} F_2(n, \gamma) + D \right] \qquad (3.5)$$

where,

$$F_1(n, \gamma) = \frac{\sin \gamma - n\gamma}{(1 - n^2)^{3/2}}$$

$$F_2(n, \gamma) = \frac{-\frac{3}{2} n\gamma + (1 + n^2) \sin \gamma - \frac{1}{4} n \sin 2\gamma}{(1 - n^2)^{5/2}}$$

Boundary Conditions

Let $p = 0, \quad \theta = \theta_1 \quad (\gamma = \gamma_1, \quad x = x_1, \quad h = h_1)$

and $p = 0, \quad \theta = \theta_2 \quad (\gamma = \gamma_2, \quad x = x_2, \quad h = h_2)$

D/H. Elasto-Hydro. Lub. 3

With these conditions the integration constants take the form

$$\frac{nh_m}{R} = \frac{-F_1(n, \gamma_1) + F_1(n, \gamma_2)}{F_2(n, \gamma_1) - F_2(n, \gamma_2)} \tag{3.6}$$

$$D = \frac{F_1(n, \gamma_1) F_2(n, \gamma_2) - F_1(n, \gamma_2) F_2(n, \gamma_1)}{F_2(n, \gamma_1) - F_2(n, \gamma_2)}$$

Normal Force Components Acting on the Cylinder and Plane

The normal (pressure) surface force components acting on the cylinder and plane are shown in Fig. 3.1. The forces acting on a unit length (in the z-direction) of the cylinder and plane are defined by the relationships,

$$P_{x1} = 0$$

$$P_{x2} = -\int_{h_1}^{h_2} p \, dh = -R \int_{\theta_1}^{\theta_2} p \sin \theta \, d\theta$$

$$P_{y_1} = \int_{x_1}^{x_2} p \, dx = R \int_{\theta_1}^{\theta_2} p \cos \theta \, d\theta$$

$$P_{y_2} = \int_{x_1}^{x_2} p \, dx = R \int_{\theta_1}^{\theta_2} p \cos \theta \, d\theta \quad (= P_{y_1})$$

$$P_1 = (P_{x_1}^2 + P_{y_1}^2)^{1/2} \quad (= P_{y_1})$$

$$P_2 = (P_{x_2}^2 + P_{y_2}^2)^{1/2}$$

$$\varphi = \tan^{-1}\left(\frac{P_{x_2}}{P_{y_2}}\right)$$

An expression for the force component P_{x_2} can readily be determined by integrating by parts

$$P_{x_2} = -R \int_{\theta_1}^{\theta_2} p \sin \theta \, d\theta$$

$$= R \left[p \cos \theta \right]_{\theta_1}^{\theta_2} - R \int_{\theta_1}^{\theta_2} \cos \theta \, \frac{dp}{d\theta} \, d\theta \tag{3.7}$$

Since $p = 0$ when $\theta = \theta_1$ and $\theta = \theta_2$ the first term on the rigth-hand side of eqn. (3.7) is zero. On introducing eqn. (3.3) into (3.7) and defining a dimensionless force coefficient,

$$\bar{P}_{x_2} = \frac{P_{x_2}}{2\eta u}$$

we obtain;

$$\bar{P}_{x_2} = 6(\theta_1 - \theta_2) - 6\left[\frac{(2n^2 - 1)\gamma - n \sin \gamma}{(1 - n^2)^{3/2}} \right.$$

$$\left. + \frac{nh_m}{R} n^2 \frac{\left\{ \dfrac{(1 + 2n^2)\gamma}{2} - 2n \sin \gamma + \dfrac{\sin 2\gamma}{4} \right\}}{(1 - n^2)^{5/2}} \right]$$

$$(3.8)$$

By a similar process the dimensionless force components acting in the y-direction can be shown to be,

$$\bar{P}_{y_1} = \bar{P}_{y_2} = -6\left[\frac{-1}{(1 + n \cos \theta)} - \ln (1 + n \cos \theta) \right.$$

$$\left. + \frac{nh_m}{R} \frac{(1 + 2n \cos \theta)}{2(1 + n \cos \theta)^2} \right]_{\theta_1}^{\theta_2}$$

$$(3.9)$$

where

$$\bar{P}_{y_1} = \frac{P_{y_1}}{2\eta u}$$

and

$$\bar{P}_{y_2} = \frac{P_{y_2}}{2\eta u}.$$

Cavitation Boundary Condition

It is convenient to consider the conditions under which the pressure curve terminates in the divergent clearance space before deriving the shear force expressions. The theoretical pressure returns to ambient at a point determined by the values attributed to nh_m/R and D in eqn. (3.5). From this point of view either of the curves (a) or (b) shown in Fig. 3.2 could represent the pressure distribution at the end of the load carrying film. However, the tendency to form sub-ambient pressures in the divergent clearance space suggested by curve (a) leads to a disruption of the lubricant film due to *cavitation*. In general two forms of

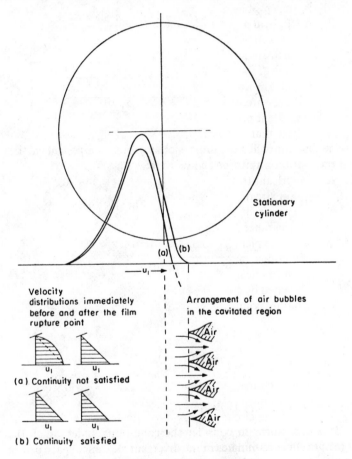

FIG. 3.2. Cavitation boundary condition.

cavitation may occur. If the pressure falls to the vapour pressure of the lubricant the liquid will boil at the reduced pressure. The low pressure bubbles formed by this process tend to collapse as they move into regions of higher pressure, and the local pressures generated by this action may lead to cavitation erosion of the bounding solids. This form of cavitation, which is well known in the field of hydraulic machinery, is rarely encountered in lubrication problems.

The usual form of cavitation in lubricating films is the liberation of dissolved gases. Mineral oils contain between 8 and 10 per cent of dissolved air, and when the pressure in the oil film falls some of the air is liberated in the form of bubbles which tend to maintain the oil film pressures near to the level of the saturation pressure. For most lubrication conditions the saturation and ambient pressures will be almost equal. These observations suggest that the pressure in the cavitated region of the lubricant film will be approximately constant and near to the atmospheric or ambient pressure. It has frequently been noted that the lubricant traverses the cavitated region of bearings in a series of thin streams separated by large air spaces as shown in Fig. 3.2. The air bubbles appear to extend almost completely across the clearance space between the bearing components, and with this simple picture in mind a brief examination of the velocity distributions immediately before, and after, the oil film rupture point indicates that only a pressure distribution of the kind represented by curve (b) of Fig. 3.2 satisfies flow continuity. The cavitation boundary condition for lubricating films thus becomes,

$$p = \frac{\mathrm{d}p}{\mathrm{d}\theta} = 0, \quad \theta = \theta_2 \tag{3.10}$$

where p is, of course, the gauge pressure.

It has been shown (Dowson, 1957) that this condition may be violated in some circumstances by the existence of small sub-ambient pressures immediately upstream of the cavitated region, but the influence of these sub-ambient pressures in highly loaded contacts will be very small indeed.

Tangential Force Components Acting on the Cylinder and Plane

It is clear that different stress equations must be employed in the load carrying and cavitated parts of the contact. The shear stresses in the cavitated region act over a small proportion of the solid surfaces due to the presence of air bubbles. If $\bar{z}$ is the fraction of the clearance space width in the z-direction occupied by lubricant it can be seen that flow continuity yields the relationship,

$$\bar{z} = \frac{h_m}{h}$$

where h_m is the film thickness at the point of maximum pressure (where $dp/dx = 0$). In general the cavitated zone will terminate at some point between x_2 and R (θ_2 and $\pi/2$), but owing to the very small width of the oil streams at large values of x the contribution to the total surface shear forces from this region is small. For convenience it will be assumed that the cavitated oil film extends to $x = R$ ($\theta = \pi/2$).

The general expressions for the tangential (viscous) forces acting on the solids then become,

$$F_1 = \int_{x_1}^{x_2} \tau_{y=0}\, dx + \int_{x_2}^{R} \bar{z}\tau_{y=0}\, dx$$

$$= R\int_{\theta_1}^{\theta_2} \tau_{y=0} \cos\theta\, d\theta + R\int_{\theta_2}^{\pi/2} \bar{z}\tau_{y=0} \cos\theta\, d\theta,$$

$$F_2 = -\int_{x_1}^{x_2} \tau_{y=h}\, dx - \int_{x_2}^{R} \bar{z}\tau_{y=h}\, dx$$

$$= -R\int_{\theta_1}^{\theta_2} \tau_{y=h} \cos\theta\, d\theta - R\int_{\theta_2}^{\pi/2} \bar{z}\tau_{y=h} \cos\theta\, d\theta$$

On introducing the velocity derivatives obtained from eqn. (2.4) we find that,

$$\tau_{y=0} = -\frac{h}{2}\frac{dp}{dx} - \eta\frac{(u_1 - u_2)}{h} \qquad \theta_1 < \theta < \theta_2$$

$$= -\eta\frac{(u_1 - u_2)}{h} \qquad \theta_2 < \theta < \frac{\pi}{2}$$

$$\tau_{y=h} = \frac{h}{2}\frac{dp}{dx} - \eta\frac{(u_1 - u_2)}{h} \qquad \theta_1 < \theta < \theta_2$$

$$= -\eta\frac{(u_1 - u_2)}{h} \qquad \theta_2 < \theta < \frac{\pi}{2}$$

hence,

$$F_1 = -\frac{1}{2}\int_{\theta_1}^{\theta_2} h\frac{dp}{d\theta}\, d\theta - \eta(u_1 - u_2)\, R\, \times$$

$$\times\left[\int_{\theta_1}^{\theta_2}\frac{\cos\theta}{h}\, d\theta + \int_{\theta_2}^{\pi/2}\frac{z}{h}\frac{\cos\theta}{h}\, d\theta\right]$$

$$F_2 = -\frac{1}{2}\int_{\theta_1}^{\theta_2} h\frac{dp}{d\theta}\, d\theta + \eta(u_1 - u_2)\, R\, \times$$

$$\times\left[\int_{\theta_1}^{\theta_2}\frac{\cos\theta}{h}\, d\theta + \int_{\theta_2}^{\pi/2}\frac{z}{h}\frac{\cos\theta}{h}\, d\theta\right]$$

Now,

$$\int_{\theta_1}^{\theta_2} h\frac{dp}{d\theta}\, d\theta = \left[hp\right]_{\theta_1}^{\theta_2} - \int_{\theta_1}^{\theta_2} p\frac{dh}{d\theta}\, d\theta$$

and since $p = 0$ when $\theta = \theta_1, \theta_2$, the first term on the right-hand side is zero. Also,

$$-\int_{\theta_1}^{\theta_2} p\frac{dh}{d\theta}\, d\theta = P_{x_2}$$

and hence,

$$\int_{\theta_1}^{\theta_2} h \frac{dp}{d\theta} \, d\theta = P_{x_2}$$

On introducing this result and evaluating the remaining integrals the dimensionless shear force parameters can be written in the form,

$$\left.\begin{aligned} \bar{F}_1 &= -\frac{\bar{P}_{x_2}}{2} - \left(\frac{u_1 - u_2}{u_1 + u_2}\right) A \\ \bar{F}_2 &= -\frac{\bar{P}_{x_2}}{2} + \left(\frac{u_1 - u_2}{u_1 + u_2}\right) A \end{aligned}\right\} \qquad (3.11)$$

where,

$$\bar{F} = \frac{F}{2\eta u}$$

and

$$A = (\theta_1 - \theta_2) + \frac{(\gamma_2 - \gamma_1)}{(1 - n^2)^{1/2}} + \frac{n^2 h_m}{R} \left\{\frac{\sin \gamma - n\gamma}{(1 - n^2)^{3/2}}\right\}_{\gamma_2}^{\gamma = \cos^{-1} n}$$

It will be noted from eqns. (3.11) that,

$$F_1 + F_2 + P_{x_2} = 0$$

—an overall equilibrium condition which must apply to the lubricant in the absence of inertia and body forces.

Volume Rate of Flow

The volume rate of flow of lubricant in the x-direction per unit width of cylinder can be found by considering the conditions at the point of maximum pressure.

$$Q = uh_m$$

thus,

$$\bar{Q} = \frac{Q}{uh_0} = \frac{h_m}{h_0} \qquad (3.12)$$

Solutions of Equations

The cavitation boundary condition discussed earlier will be employed and the cavitated region will be considered to extend to $\theta = \pi/2$. In addition it will be assumed that pressure generation commences at $\theta = -\pi/2$.

For the pressure gradient to be zero at some value of θ_2 eqn. (3.3) shows that,

$$\frac{nh_m}{R} = -(1 + n\cos\theta_2) = \frac{-(1 - n^2)}{(1 - n\cos\gamma_2)} \qquad (3.13)$$

If the pressure itself is also zero at this point eqn. (3.6) and the present inlet boundary condition require that,

$$\frac{nh_m}{R} = \frac{-F_1(n, \cos^{-1}(n)) + F_1(n, \gamma_2)}{F_2(n, \cos^{-1}(n)) - F_2(n, \gamma_2)} \qquad (3.14)$$

On equating (3.13) and (3.14) an equation is formed which relates γ_2 to n. Once this equation has been solved all the previous expressions for the dimensionless force components and flow rates can be evaluated. Values of the dimensionless parameters for various values of s are presented in Table 3.2.

An examination of Table 3.2 suggests that good approximations to the dimensionless force coefficients at high values of R/h_0 can be written as follows,

$$\left. \begin{aligned}
\bar{P}_{x_1} &= 0 & \bar{P}_{x_2} &= 4\cdot5\left(\frac{R}{h_0}\right)^{1/2} \\[2mm]
\bar{P}_{y_1} &= 2\cdot45\,\frac{R}{h_0} & \bar{P}_{y_2} &= 2\cdot45\,\frac{R}{h_0} \\[2mm]
\bar{F}_1 &= -\frac{\bar{P}_{x_2}}{2} - \left(\frac{u_1 - u_2}{u_1 + u_2}\right)3\cdot48\left(\frac{R}{h_0}\right)^{1/2} \\[2mm]
\bar{F}_2 &= -\frac{\bar{P}_{x_2}}{2} + \left(\frac{u_1 - u_2}{u_1 + u_2}\right)3\cdot48\left(\frac{R}{h_0}\right)^{1/2}
\end{aligned} \right\} \qquad (3.15)$$

TABLE 3.2

$s\left(=\dfrac{R}{h_0}\right)$	θ_2^0	$\bar{P}_{x_1}$	$\bar{P}_{x_2}$	$\bar{P}_{y_1}=\bar{P}_{y_2}=\bar{P}_1$	$\bar{P}_2$	φ^0	A	$\bar{Q}$
10	11·31	0	4·608	13·99	14·72	18·24	9·298	1·194
10^2	3·82	0	32·54	221·5	223·8	8·36	32·95	1·222
10^3	1·22	0	130·7	2411	2414	3·10	108·4	1·226
10^4	0·385	0	444·9	24,424	24,428	1·04	347·0	1·226
10^5	0·122	0	1439	244,700	244,700	0·337	1102	1·226
10^6	0·039	0	4543	2,451,000	2,451,000	0·106	3490	1·226

These simple expressions are very useful in the analysis of lightly loaded rollers. They will be employed in Chapter 4 when the film thickness in lubricated rigid contacts is considered.

The angle θ_2 which locates the oil film rupture point can be expressed in terms of (R/h_0) as follows.

$$\theta_2 \approx 38 \cdot 5/(R/h_0)^{1/2} \text{ deg}$$

or

$$\theta_2 \approx 0 \cdot 672/(R/h_0)^{1/2} \text{ rad} \tag{3.16}$$

Now for a circular cylinder,

$$\frac{h}{h_0} = 1 + \frac{R}{h_0}(1 - \cos\theta)$$

and on introducing a series representation for $\cos\theta$

$$\frac{h}{h_0} = 1 + \frac{R}{h_0}\left(\frac{\theta^2}{2!} - \frac{\theta^4}{4!} + \frac{\theta^6}{6!} \dots\right) \tag{3.17}$$

The ratio of the film thickness at the oil film rupture point (h_m) to the minimum film thickness (h_0) is found by introducing the approximate expression for θ_2 from (3.16) into (3.17)

$$\frac{h_m}{h_0} \approx 1 + \frac{(0\cdot672)^2}{2!} - \frac{(0\cdot672)^4}{4!}\left(\frac{h_0}{R}\right) + \dots$$

or

$$\frac{h_m}{h_0} \approx 1 \cdot 23 \tag{3.18}$$

Solution of the Reynolds Equation for a Rigid Parabolic Cylinder and Plane

The solution for a parabolic cylinder is well known (see for example, Martin, 1916, and Purday, 1949) and hence the results will be summarized here.

For the geometry of a cylinder near a plane shown in Fig. 3.1 the parabolic approximation employs the following film thickness relationship,

$$h \approx h_0 + \frac{x^2}{2R}$$

Purday (1949) has calculated force coefficients for numerous cases, and for the particular boundary conditions employed here for the extent of the pressure curve we can write his results in the following form,

$$
\left.
\begin{aligned}
\bar{P}_{x_1} &= 0 & \bar{P}_{x_2} &= 4 \cdot 58 \left(\frac{R}{h_0}\right)^{1/2} \\[2mm]
\bar{P}_{y_1} &= 2 \cdot 44 \, \frac{R}{h_0} & \bar{P}_{y_2} &= 2 \cdot 44 \, \frac{R}{h_0} \\[2mm]
\bar{F}_1 &= - \frac{\bar{P}_{x2}}{2} - \left(\frac{u_1 - u_2}{u_1 + u_2}\right) 2 \cdot 84 \left(\frac{R}{h_0}\right)^{1/2} \\[2mm]
\bar{F}_2 &= - \frac{\bar{P}_{x2}}{2} + \left(\frac{u_1 - u_2}{u_1 + u_2}\right) 2 \cdot 84 \left(\frac{R}{h_0}\right)^{1/2}
\end{aligned}
\right\}
\qquad (3.19)
$$

From eqns. (3.15) and (3.19) it can be seen that the difference between the calculated normal force components for the circular and parabolic cylinders is negligible. The difference between the coefficients 3·48 and 2·84 in the friction force expressions arises from the assumptions made about the influence of the cavitated region on surface shear forces. In the case of the circular cylinder a maximum allowance for the shear stresses within the thin streams of continuous lubricant in the cavitated region has been included. In Purday's parabolic cylinder analysis the shear stresses within the cavitated zone were omitted.

If the lubrication conditions are such that the shear forces in the cavitated part of the divergent clearance space make a maximum contribution to the total friction force compatible with the cavitation boundary condition discussed earlier, the sliding friction force component is increased by about 23 per cent. Dowson and Higginson (1963) have demonstrated that this difference can lead to significant changes in the predicted motion of rollers subjected to small torques in a roller bearing assembly.

CHAPTER 4

FILM THICKNESS IN HIGHLY LOADED RIGID CONTACTS

IT HAS been shown in Chapter 1 that many machine contacts can be represented by cylinders. Furthermore, when the problem is reduced to the geometry of an equivalent cylinder near a plane, the film shape can be adequately represented by either a circular or parabolic profile. If the components of a machine contact are to be effectively lubricated, the film thickness must be significant compared with the surface roughness of the solids. This condition can be examined in the case of rigid components by applying the results obtained in Chapter 3. The force component equations for a lubricated rigid contact (3.15) can be rearranged to give the following film thickness formula,

$$\frac{h_0}{R} = 4 \cdot 9 \, \frac{\eta u}{P_y} \qquad (4.1)$$

This formula will be used to calculate the film thickness in two representative machine contacts, namely *gear teeth* and *roller bearings*.

For a gear tooth contact at the pitch point, typical values for the viscosity, surface speeds and loads are,

$$\eta = 0 \cdot 075 \text{ Pa s}$$

$$u_1 = u_2 = 5 \text{ m/s (197 in./s)}.$$

thus

$$u = \frac{(u_1 + u_2)}{2} = 5 \text{ m/s (197 in./s)}$$

$$P_y = 2 \cdot 5 \text{ Mn/m (14,275 lbf/in.)}$$

With these values the film thickness ratio given by eqn. (4.1) is,

$$\frac{h_0}{R} = 0.735 \times 10^{-6} \qquad (4.2)$$

A representative radius of the equivalent cylinder in a gear contact is 20 mm, and hence,

$$h_0 = 0.015 \ \mu\text{m} \ (0.58 \ \mu\text{in.})$$

This film thickness is very small; even compared with the best surface finishes encountered in gears. The conclusion to be drawn at this stage is that hydrodynamic theory for rigid contacts fails to predict the existence of satisfactory lubricating films in gears. In the case of rolling contact bearings the following example is typical.

The load capacity of a cylindrical roller bearing designed for a life of 1000 hr when operating at a speed of 5000 rev/min (524 rad/s) on a 50 mm (1.97 in.) dia. shaft results in a maximum roller load of about 0.3 Mn/m (1713 lbf/in.). The viscosity of a typical lubricant at the bearing operating temperature would be 0.01 Pa s. The radius of the inner track is approximately 32 mm (1.26 in.) and if the roller radius is 8 mm (0.315 in.) the radius of the equivalent cylinder near a plane becomes

$$R = \frac{R_1 r}{r + R_1} = \frac{32 \times 8}{(32 + 8)} = 6.4 \ \text{mm} \ (0.252 \ \text{in})$$

In pure rolling the sum of the surface velocities at the contact between the roller and inner race can readily be determined by reference to Fig. 12.1. If ω_c is the angular velocity of a roller centre about the bearing centre and ω the angular velocity of a roller about its own centre measured in relation to rotating axes $X \, O' \, Y$, then, as shown in Chapter 12,

$$\omega_c = \frac{\Omega}{2(1 + s)}$$

$$\omega = \frac{(1 + 2s)}{2s(1 + s)} \Omega$$

where

$$s = \frac{r}{R_1}$$

Hence

$$u = \frac{u_1 + u_2}{2} = \frac{R_1(\Omega - \omega_c) + r\omega}{2}$$

or

$$u = \frac{R_1\Omega}{2} \frac{\left(1 + 2\,\dfrac{r}{R_1}\right)}{\left(1 + \dfrac{r}{R_1}\right)}$$

For the present example,

$$u = 10{\cdot}05 \text{ m/s (396 in./s)}$$

The film thickness ratio is thus found from eqn. (4.1) to be,

$$\frac{h_0}{R} = 1{\cdot}64 \times 10^{-6}$$

The minimum film thickness is thus $0{\cdot}011$ μm ($0{\cdot}41$ μin.). The surface roughness of standard roller bearings is about $0{\cdot}25$ μm (10 μin.) (tracks) and $0{\cdot}13$ μm (5 μin.) (rollers) c.l.a. The calculated film thickness is far too small to provide any support for the idea that the components may be separated by a continuous film of lubricant.

These two examples illustrate the state of lubrication theory as applied to highly loaded contacts some fifteen or twenty years ago. On the one hand operating experience suggested that many highly loaded contacts were protected by fluid films, and yet on the other hand hydrodynamic theory failed to predict the existence of oil films which were of the required thickness. This situation posed a problem which was at once intriguing and difficult. The conflict was only removed after many years of careful theoretical and experimental investigation.

Clearly it is necessary to re-examine the assumptions made in the present analysis and to estimate the relative importance of effects which have been neglected. Amongst the factors which have been omitted and which may influence the calculation of film thickness are thermal effects, side-leakage, non-Newtonian behaviour of the lubricant and high pressure effects. In the latter case the influence of high pressure on both the lubricant and the bounding solids must be considered. In this examination we are seeking an effect which will lead to an increase in the predicted film thickness.

Thermal Effects

The temperature in highly loaded contacts may be considerably in excess of the ambient temperature, and since the viscosity of most lubricants decreases as the temperature rises, the effective viscosity in the contact will be reduced below the corresponding value for an isothermal contact. It is clear from eqn. (4.1) that the film thickness in a contact formed by rigid components is directly proportional to the lubricant viscosity, and hence an increase in lubricant temperature will diminish the film thickness.

There is, however, another thermal action which should be mentioned at this stage. It is known that thermal expansion of the lubricant can influence the performance of parallel surface thrust bearings; the so-called "thermal wedge" mechanism. This action, which relies upon the change in density of the lubricant as it passes through the contact, cannot be expected to contribute significantly to the hydrodynamic load carrying capacity. From these observations it is clear that thermal effects cannot be expected to improve the film thickness prediction.

Side-leakage

In the study of conventional hydrodynamic bearings it is well known that side-leakage reduces the load carrying capacity for a given minimum film thickness. The load carrying capacity of a lubricated cylindrical contact will be similarly affected, and it is clear that side-leakage will produce the reverse of the effect we are seeking.

Non-Newtonian Behaviour of the Lubricant

It has been suggested that non-Newtonian behaviour of the lubricant may produce an increased load carrying capacity in some lubricated contacts. This suggestion has been examined by Milne (1957) and by Tanner (1960) for rigid cylinders. Although these investigations considered different stress-deformation laws, they both predicted a reduction in the load carrying capacity of a bearing of given oil film geometry. Both authors consider the lubricant to behave like a Maxwellian fluid, and Milne points out that visco-elastic effects are likely to be of importance whenever the transit time required for the lubricant to pass through the loaded region of a contact is comparable with the *relaxation time* of the fluid (T) defined by the ratio (η/G). In this ratio η is the viscosity and G the shear modulus of the lubricant.

Barlow and Lamb (1959) have examined the visco-elastic behaviour of lubricating oils under cyclic shearing stress. A typical value of T for mineral oils appears to be about 10^{-8} sec. This suggests that, if the loaded region of the contact is only 25 μm (10^{-3} in.) in length, relaxation behaviour will not be significant until surface speeds of the order of 2500 m/s (0.98×10^5 in./s) are encountered. However, it is worth noting that Milne found a deviation from Newtonian behaviour at transit times of about 100 times the relaxation time. Tanner formed a dimensionless group (TU/h) by multiplying the relaxation time by the shear rate (U/h), and he noted that his solutions were valid for values of this parameter up to about 0.3. For a film thickness of 0.5 μm (19.7 μin.) this corresponds to a surface speed of 15 m/s (591 in./s). In this range of conditions Tanner found that the effect of non-Newtonian behaviour on load carrying capacity was quite small.

Burton (1960) also examined the influence of visco-elastic effects in the lubrication of rolling contacts. For a Maxwellian fluid Burton concluded that the load capacity and maximum shear stress might suffer sizeable reductions, in pure rolling. Burton's results were presented in terms of a relaxation number defined as $TU/(h_0 R)^{1/2}$.

Bell (1962) considered non-Newtonian behaviour by adopting a Ree–Eyring (1955) model for the lubricant. This model allows the shear stress to develop at a lessening rate as the shear rate increases. The relationship between shear stress and shear rate is,

$$\tau = \frac{X}{\alpha} \sinh^{-1}\left(\beta \frac{\partial u}{\partial y}\right) \tag{4.3}$$

where

$$X = X_0 \, e^{\gamma_1 p}$$

and

$$\beta = \beta_0 \, e^{\gamma_2 p}$$

The quantities α, X_0, β_0, γ_1 and γ_2 are constant at a given temperature.

For values of $(\beta \, \partial u/\partial y)$ which are very small compared with unity $\sinh^{-1}(\beta \, \partial u/\partial y) \approx \beta \frac{\partial u}{\partial y}$, and eqn. (4.3) can then be written as,

$$\tau = \eta \left(\frac{\partial u}{\partial y}\right) \tag{4.4}$$

where

$$\eta = \frac{X}{\alpha} \beta$$

Equation (4.4) is a statment of the relationship between shear stress and shear rate for a Newtonian fluid.

Bell found that the computed film thickness for a Ree–Eyring fluid was much smaller than the film thickness predicted by Grubin for a Newtonian lubricant. Indeed, whereas the Grubin theory over-estimates the film thickness the Ree–Eyring theory seems to predict results considerably smaller than the available experimental values. One of the serious limitations in the application of Ree–Eyring theory is the lack of data on the parameters employed.

From this discussion it is clear that the non-Newtonian behaviour of lubricating oils is likely to lead to a reduction in minimum film thickness for a given load. Furthermore, the calculations suggest that some lubricated contacts may be operating under conditions in which the relaxation behaviour of the lubricant is important.

High Pressure Effects

For a highly loaded lubricated cylinder near a plane, the width of the effective load carrying film is small compared with the radius of the cylinder. Since the radius of the equivalent cylinder is often of the order of 0·02 m, or less, it is clear that very high local pressure will be generated in the lubricant. These high pressures will influence both the lubricant and the solid bearing components.

The two significant lubricant properties which will be affected by high pressures are density and viscosity. The density of liquid lubricants may increase by about 20 per cent at exceedingly high pressures. Changes of this order of magnitude cannot be expected to affect materially the separation of the bearing surfaces, and in any event the result will not be beneficial. The viscosity of lubricants is also pressure dependent, and under isothermal conditions a simple exponential relationship gives a reasonable approximation to the viscosity–pressure characteristics of a liquid. The value of the coefficient in eqn. (4.5) is such that a viscosity change of one thousandfold is obtained with a pressure rise of about 310 MN/m² (20 tonf/in²).

$$\eta = \eta_0 \exp(\alpha p) \qquad (4.5)$$

When this particular pressure–viscosity relationship is employed, the integrated Reynolds equation has the form,

$$\exp(-\alpha p)\frac{dp}{dx} = 12\,\eta_0\,u\left[\frac{h - h_m}{h^3}\right] \qquad (4.6)$$

The right-hand side of eqn. (4.6) clearly represents the pressure gradient in an isoviscous lubricant of viscosity η_0. If the pressure generated by an isoviscous lubricant is denoted by q, the relationship between the pressure p in a fluid of variable viscosity

and q is at once apparent. The quantity q is known as the
reduced pressure.

$$\exp\left(-\alpha p\right)\frac{\mathrm{d}p}{\mathrm{d}x} = -\frac{1}{\alpha}\frac{\mathrm{d}}{\mathrm{d}x}\exp\left(-\alpha p\right) = \frac{\mathrm{d}q}{\mathrm{d}x}$$

hence, since $q = 0$ when $p = 0$,

$$\exp\left(-\alpha p\right) = 1 - \alpha q$$

or

$$p = -\frac{1}{\alpha}\ln\left(1 - \alpha q\right) \tag{4.7}$$

The solution for q has been presented in Chapter 3 (eqn. (3.5))
and eqn. (4.7) shows that the pressure in a lubricant exhibiting the
pressure–viscosity characteristics represented by eqn. (4.5) can be
determined directly from the isoviscous solution. The pressure
in the lubricant of variable viscosity is everywhere greater than
the pressure in an isoviscous fluid.

An interesting feature of eqn. (4.7) is that the pressure becomes
infinite when q has a value $1/\alpha$. Within the limitations imposed
upon the present analysis the value of the film thickness which
produces this value of q represents a limiting value. Blok (1952)
has evaluated the relative load carrying capacities of an isoviscous
lubricant and a lubricant exhibiting an exponential viscosity–
pressure characteristic under these limiting conditions, and he
found that the ratio of the capacities was about 2·3 in favour of
the variable viscosity fluid. In this limiting case the film thickness
formula (4.1) can be written as,

$$\left(\frac{h_0}{R}\right)_{\mathrm{lim}} \approx 2\cdot3 \times 4\cdot9\,\frac{\eta u}{P_y} \tag{4.8}$$

Gatcombe (1945), Hersey and Lowdenslager (1950), Cameron (1952) and McEwen (1952) have also demonstrated
theoretically the beneficial effects of high pressures on lubricant
viscosity. Although several different viscosity–pressure relationships were employed and the boundary conditions adopted
by different workers for the pressure curve were not the same,
the overall results were consistent with Blok's (1952) analysis.

The influence of pressure on viscosity is the first factor we have encountered which yields in increase in the predicted film thickness. The increase of about 130 per cent calculated above is substantial, but it is still not sufficient to bring the predicted film thickness safely above the values of surface roughness in many contacts which are known to operate hydrodynamically. This brief examination does, however, show that a satisfactory analysis of highly loaded lubricated contacts must include the effect of high pressure on viscosity.

The very high, and in some cases infinite, pressures predicted above are calculated within the assumption that the bearing materials are rigid solids. Clearly, real bearing materials will deform under the action of high local pressures and the influence of this deformation must be examined.

In general terms it can be seen at once that local elastic deformation will increase the film thickness. Elastic deformations tend to increase the effective local radius of curvature of the equivalent cylinder (R) and eqn. (4.1) indicates that the separation of the surfaces is proportional to (R). The combined effect of high pressure on the lubricant and the elastic bearing solids was demonstrated in a remarkable analysis by Grubin (1949).

In outline Grubin's analysis develops as follows. Consider an elastic cylinder, which possesses a modulus of elasticity equivalent to the elastic properties of the contacting solids, to be pressed against a rigid plane as shown in Fig. 4.1. The cylinder will be flattened against the plane over the Hertzian contact zone and the contour of the cylinder outside the zone will also change. Now imagine the deformed cylinder to be lifted from the plane to give a minimum separation h_0 over the Hertzian contact zone. If the local elastic flattening in the contact is large compared with h_0, the pressure distribution in the contact must be near Hertzian, the deviation from the semi-elliptical pressure distribution required to accommodate any variation in film thickness being quite negligible. In these conditions the geometry of the lubricant film in a lubricated contact must be close to the form calculated for dry contact.

By using the shape of the deformed cylinder $(h - h_0)$ outside the contact zone it is possible to determine the pressure distribution for any value of h_0. Grubin determined the value of h_0 which produced an infinite pressure at the inlet edge of the Hertzian zone; due allowance being made for the influence of

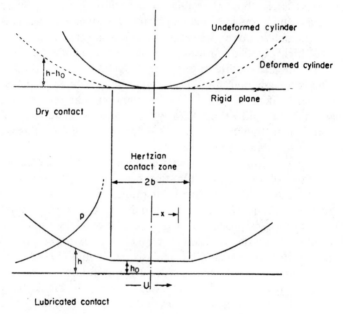

Fig. 4.1. Grubin's model of an elasto-hydrodynamic contact.

pressure on viscosity. At this point the pressure in an isoviscous lubricant would have a value $1/\alpha$, and in this respect the approach is similar to the limit analysis for rigid cylinders discussed earlier. Grubin produced an expression for h_0 which can be written in the form,

$$\frac{h_0}{R} = 1 \cdot 95 \frac{(\eta_0 u \alpha)^{8/11} E'^{1/11}}{R^{7/11} P_y^{1/11}} \tag{4.9}$$

where E' represents the elastic properties of an equivalent cylinder near a rigid plane. If suffices 1 and 2 refer to the two solids in the initial contact,

$$\frac{1}{E'} = \frac{1}{2}\left[\frac{1 - \sigma_1^2}{E_1} + \frac{1 - \sigma_2^2}{E_2}\right]$$

where E and σ represent the modulus of elasticity and Poisson's ratio respectively. A full discussion of Grubin's analysis is given in Chapter 6.

The ratio of the film thicknesses calculated according to eqn. (4.9) and (4.1) becomes,

$$\frac{h_0 \text{ (elastic, variable viscosity)}}{h_0 \text{ (rigid, constant viscosity)}} = 0.398 \frac{\alpha^{8/11} E'^{1/11} P y^{10/11}}{R^{7/11}(\eta_0 u)^{3/11}} \quad (4.10)$$

Now for steel $E' \approx 228$ G Pa (33×10^6 lb/in²) and for mineral oils a typical value of α is 0.022 μm²/N (1.5×10^{-4} in²/lb.). Hence in Nm units the product of $\alpha^{8/11} E'^{1/11}$ for a steel contact lubricated by a mineral oil is approximately 2.88×10^{-5}.

For the gear tooth problem considered at the beginning of the chapter the ratio of the film thickness on a 20 mm radius equivalent cylinder is found from eqn. (4.10) to be,

$$\frac{h_0 \text{ (elastic, variable viscosity)}}{h_0 \text{ (rigid, constant viscosity)}} = 118$$

The corresponding ratio for the roller bearing, this time with an equivalent cylinder radius of 6.4 mm, is found to be approximately 51. These ratios demonstrate the tremendous combined effect of pressure dependent viscosity and elastic deformation on film thickness. Clearly both factors have to be included in a satisfactory analysis of highly loaded contacts. The predicted minimum film thicknesses are now of the correct order for satisfactory fluid film operation, and theory and practice are no longer in conflict.

The results obtained by Grubin in his relatively simple analysis must of course be confirmed by experiment and complete theoretical solutions before they can be used with confidence. It should be recalled that the ratios calculated above are based upon Grubin's approximate analysis. They will be re-examined in the light of a full elasto-hydrodynamic analysis in Chapter 7. Furthermore, there are features of the contact mechanism which do not emerge from Grubin's film thickness analysis. The problem can no longer be treated as a hydrodynamic exercise employing rigid boundaries. The basic equations governing displacements in the elastic bearing materials must enter the analysis, and a solution must be sought which satisfactorily covers the elastic and hydrodynamic requirements of the problem. The basic hydrodynamic equations have been derived in Chapter 2, and the fundamental equations of elasticity will now be considered.

CHAPTER 5

ELASTICITY

THE next task is to calculate the stresses and displacements in the solids in contàct. The geometry of the contact leads to a number of simplifying assumptions. We are concerned only with nominal line contact in which the width of the pressure zone is very small compared with the radius and length of the solids (about a hundredth part or less). So the stresses and displacements are uniform along the length, except near the ends, and

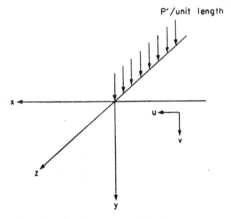

P'/unit length

FIG. 5.1. Line load on semi-infinite solid.

the solids are in a condition of *plane strain*. In addition it is permissible to calculate the stresses and displacements for a semi-infinite flat solid and to add the displacements to the curved surface of the roller; this is the usual simplification of contact problems. The tangential displacement of the surface plays no significant part when the solids are separated by a lubricating film.

The starting point is the Boussinesq function for the stresses due to a normal line load on the surface of a semi-infinite solid (see Fig. 5.1). The stresses and displacements under this load can be integrated to give the corresponding quantities under a distributed pressure. The function is, in polar coordinates,

$$\varphi = -\frac{P'}{\pi} r\theta \sin \theta$$

The stress components are given by

$$p_r = \frac{1}{r^2} \frac{\partial^2 \varphi}{\partial \theta^2} + \frac{1}{r} \frac{\partial \varphi}{\partial r} : p_\theta = \frac{\partial^2 \varphi}{\partial r^2} : q_{r\theta} = -\frac{\partial}{\partial r} \left(\frac{1}{r} \frac{\partial \varphi}{\partial \theta} \right)$$

which are, in this case,

$$p_r = -\frac{2P'}{\pi} \frac{\cos \theta}{r}, \qquad p_\theta = 0, \quad q_{r\theta} = 0,$$

a field of radial compressive stress directed towards the line of application of the load.

It is convenient in the present problem to use cartesian coordinates, when the stress function becomes

$$\varphi = -\frac{P'}{\pi} x \tan^{-1} \frac{x}{y}$$

and the stress field

$$p_x = \frac{\partial^2 \varphi}{\partial y^2} = -\frac{2P'x^2 y}{\pi(x^2 + y^2)^2}$$

$$p_y = \frac{\partial^2 \varphi}{\partial x^2} = -\frac{2P'y^3}{\pi(x^2 + y^2)^2}$$

$$q_{xy} = -\frac{\partial^2 \varphi}{\partial x \partial y} = -\frac{2P'xy^2}{\pi(x^2 + y^2)^2}$$

The Displacements

To calculate the displacements (u, v in the x-, y-directions) due to this line load we recall *Hooke's law* and the definition of strain: in plain strain

$$e_x = \frac{\partial u}{\partial x} = \frac{1}{E}\{p_x - \sigma(p_y + p_z)\}$$

$$e_y = \frac{\partial v}{\partial y} = \frac{1}{E}\{p_y - \sigma(p_z + p_x)\}$$

$$e_z = 0 = \frac{1}{E}\{p_z - \sigma(p_x + p_y)\}$$

$$e_{xy} = \frac{\partial u}{\partial y} + \frac{\partial v}{\partial x} = \frac{q_{yy}}{G} = \frac{2(1 + \sigma)}{E}q_{xy}$$

These lead straightforwardly to

$$u = \alpha \int p_x \, dx + \beta \int p_y \, dx + f(y)$$

$$v = \alpha \int p_y \, dy + \beta \int p_x \, dy + f_1(x)$$

where $f(y)$ and $f_1(x)$ are functions of y and x only, respectively, and

$$\alpha = \frac{1 - \sigma^2}{E}, \quad \beta = -\frac{\sigma(1 + \sigma)}{E}$$

The integrations give

$$u = -\frac{P'}{\pi}\left[(\alpha + \beta)\tan^{-1}\frac{x}{y} - (\alpha - \beta)\frac{xy}{x^2 + y^2}\right] + f(y) \quad (5.1)$$

$$v = -\frac{P'}{\pi}\left[\alpha\left\{\ln(x^2 + y^2) - \frac{y^2}{x^2 + y^2}\right\} - \beta\frac{x^2}{x^2 + y^2}\right] + f_1(x)$$

$$(5.2)$$

By symmetry,

$$-u(-x) = u(x)$$

So

$$f(y) = 0$$

To find $f_1(x)$, we employ

$$\frac{2(1 + \sigma)}{E} q_{xy} = 2(\alpha - \beta) q_{xy} = \frac{\partial u}{\partial y} + \frac{\partial v}{\partial x}$$

This gives

$$\frac{\partial}{\partial x} f_1(x) = 0$$

So

$$f_1(x) = \text{constant}$$

Expressions (5.1) and (5.2) give the displacements anywhere in the body due to a line load at the origin. For a strip of pressure p, width ds, on a line $x = s$, $y = 0$, the displacement in the y-direction, i.e. the normal displacement, will be

$$v = -\frac{p \, ds}{\pi} \left[\alpha \left\{ \ln \left[(x - s)^2 + y^2\right] - \frac{y^2}{(x - s)^2 + y^2} \right\} \right.$$

$$\left. - \frac{\beta(x - s)^2}{(x - s)^2 + y^2} \right] + \text{constant}$$

The displacement due to a variable pressure $p(s)$ between $x = s_1$ and $x = s_2$ can be found by integrating this expression. In particular, at the surface, where $y = 0$

$$v = -\frac{\alpha}{\pi} \int_{s_1}^{s_2} p(s) \ln (x - s)^2 \, ds + \text{constant} \qquad (5.3)$$

EXAMPLE. The deflection of the surface under a uniformly distributed pressure p_0, extending from $s = -b$ to $s = +b$, is given by

$$v = -\frac{\alpha p_0}{\pi} \int_{-b}^{b} \ln (x - s)^2 \, ds + \text{constant}$$

hence

$$v = \frac{2\alpha p_0}{\pi} [(x - b) \ln |x - b| - (x + b) \ln |x + b|]$$

$$+ \text{constant}$$

The tangential displacement of the surface is

$$u = (\alpha + \beta) p_0 \times \begin{cases} -b, \, x \geqq b \\ -x, \, b \geqq x \geqq -b \\ b, \, -b \geqq x \end{cases}$$

The log term in the normal displacement is often an embarrassment, particularly in numerical integration. In addition it implies an infinite displacement at $x = $ infinity, although being a log term it goes to infinity very slowly. While this is distressing, the reason is easy to see. In the two-dimensional problem the stresses and therefore the strains are proportional to $1/r$, giving displacements proportional to $\ln r$. In contrast, in the three-dimensional point contact, the stresses and strains are proportional to $1/r^2$, giving displacements proportional to $1/r$, which vanish at infinity.

The displacement under an arbitrary pressure distribution cannot be found by straightforward numerical integration because at $x = s$ the integrand goes to minus infinity. Various devices have been used to overcome this difficulty; see for instance Poritsky (1952), Weber and Saalfeld (1954) and Archard, Gair and Hist (1961). As we have seen in the example above, when the pressure can be expressed as a function which permits formal integration, the displacement is continuous and finite in the region of the load. In general, if the pressure distribution is represented by a polynomial

$$p = p_0 \sum_{n=0,1\ldots} A_n s^n$$

the integral can be evaluated.

$$\int_{s_1}^{s_2} s^n \ln (x - s)^2 \, ds = f_n \text{ say}$$

$$= \frac{2}{n + 1} \left\{ (s_2^{n+1} - x^{n+1}) \ln |x - s_2| - (s_1^{n+1} - x^{n+1}) \ln |x - s_1| \right.$$

$$- \frac{1}{n + 1} (s_2^{n+1} - s_1^{n+1}) - \frac{1}{n} x(s_2^n - s_1^n) \cdots$$

$$\left. \cdots - \frac{1}{2} x^{n-1}(s_2^2 - s_1^2) - x^n(s_2 - s_1) \right\}$$

The expression for the displacement becomes

$$\frac{\pi v}{\alpha p_0} + \text{constant} = \sum_{n=0,1\ldots} A_n f_n \tag{5.4}$$

The first three terms of the series suffice for accurate computation and are fairly easy to handle.

The Stresses

Two solids in dry contact provide the best-known example of this sort of problem. In the case of two cylinders in nominal line contact, the distribution of normal surface stress at the contact is semi-elliptical. Contours of maximum principal stress difference, given by Poritsky (1950), are shown in Fig. 5.2. Under a uniformly distributed pressure, the stress field is somewhat different; contours of maximum principal stress difference are shown in Fig. 5.3.

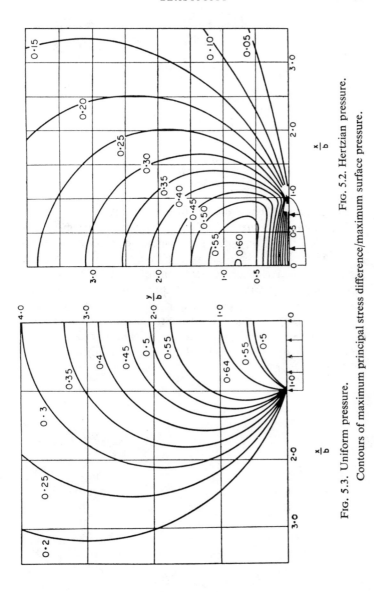

Fig. 5.2. Hertzian pressure.

Fig. 5.3. Uniform pressure.

Contours of maximum principal stress difference/maximum surface pressure.

For an arbitrary pressure distribution the stresses must in general be evaluated numerically. The components are

$$p_x = -\frac{2}{\pi} \int_{s_1}^{s_2} \frac{(x - s)^2 \, yp(s) \, \mathrm{d}s}{[(x - s)^2 + y^2]^2}$$

$$p_y = -\frac{2}{\pi} \int_{s_1}^{s_2} \frac{y^3 p(s) \, \mathrm{d}s}{[(x - s)^2 + y^2]^2}$$

$$q_{xy} = -\frac{2}{\pi} \int_{s_1}^{s_2} \frac{(x - s) \, y^2 p(s) \, \mathrm{d}s}{[(x - s)^2 + y^2]^2}$$

The integrals could be evaluated directly by a numerical process such as Simpson's method. The danger with Simpson in this case is that the *integrand* is represented by segments of parabolas, whereas it is the *pressure distribution* which is accessible for inspection. However, if a segment of the pressure curve is represented by a parabolic arc, the expressions can be integrated formally. The result is cumbersome, but readily amenable to automatic computing, and much more reliable than a straightforward numerical integration of the original expression. The procedure is described in detail by Dowson, Higginson and Whitaker (1963).

CHAPTER 6

ELASTO-HYDRODYNAMIC THEORY

This chapter is devoted to the methods which have been employed to solve the elasto-hydrodynamic problem, in particular to that used by the authors. The problem has been discussed in some detail earlier and the relevant effects examined separately, so it remains only to seek a solution which reconciles the hydrodynamic and the elastic equations. The problem is to calculate the pressure distribution in the contact, allowing at the same time for the effects that this pressure will have on the properties of the fluid and on the geometry of the solids. The solution will also provide the shape of the lubricant film, in particular the minimum clearance between the solids. First the *assumptions* are set down, although some of these have been discussed earlier.

(1) The displacements are calculated for a semi-infinite solid in a condition of plane strain.

(2) Side-leakage is neglected. This is justified by the dimensional proportions of the pressure region — the zone width is very small compared with the length of the cylinder. Also, because the film thickness is small compared with the displacements, any closing of the gap near the ends of the cylinders will have little effect on the pressure; hence $\partial p / \partial z$ will be small.

(3) The boundary conditions for pressure are: at inlet $p = 0$ at a large distance from the high pressure zone; at outlet $p = \partial p / \partial x = 0$.

(4) The lubricant is incompressible. In the later solutions below this restriction is removed.

(5) Thermal effects are neglected. These are the variation of viscosity of the lubricant with temperature and the thermal ex-

pansion of the lubricant and the cylinders. These effects are discussed in another chapter.

The equations to be solved are:

$$\frac{\mathrm{d}}{\mathrm{d}x}\left(\frac{h^3}{\eta}\frac{\mathrm{d}p}{\mathrm{d}x}\right) = 12u\frac{\mathrm{d}h}{\mathrm{d}x}$$

$$\eta = f(p) \tag{6.1}$$

$$h = h_0 + \frac{x^2}{2R} + v$$

v is the combined displacement of the two solids and is therefore

$$v = -\frac{2}{\pi E'}\int_{s_1}^{s_2} p(s)\ln(x-s)^2\,\mathrm{d}s + \text{constant} \tag{6.2}$$

where

$$\frac{1}{E'} = \frac{1}{2}\left[\frac{1-\sigma_1^2}{E_1} + \frac{1-\sigma_2^2}{E_2}\right]$$

If the variation of viscosity with pressure is represented by the exponential

$$\eta = \eta_0 \exp(\alpha p)$$

it is convenient to replace the pressure p as the independent variable in the Reynolds equation by the so-called reduced pressure q.

$$q = \frac{1}{\alpha}\{1 - \exp(-\alpha p)\}$$

$$\frac{\mathrm{d}q}{\mathrm{d}x} = \exp(-\alpha p)\frac{\mathrm{d}p}{\mathrm{d}x} \tag{6.3}$$

q is therefore equal to the pressure which would be generated in a fluid with constant viscosity η_0, all other things being unaltered.

These simultaneous equations constitute the standard iso-thermal problem, and a number of attempts at a solution have been made. A full analytical solution has not yet been found, but a number of useful results have come from numerical work. The defiance of the problem lies in the fact that a straight iteration on the lines, assumed pressure → deformation → film shape → pressure, does not always converge. Sternlicht, Lewis and Flynn (1960) claim that, with the equations in finite difference form, the massive computation on these lines converges; unfortunately the details of their results are not available. Archard, Gair and Hirst (1961) describe a process in which convergence is achieved in low–medium speed and high load conditions by imposing certain features on the pressure distribution. This is a very useful approximate method and the paper gives some interesting results. Osterle and Stephenson (1962) have also outlined a direct procedure which can be made to converge at low loads. The process is essentially that of a straight iteration along the lines mentioned above but, unfortunately, for loads which are only modest by elasto-hydrodynamic standards an excessive number of cycles of calculation is required. A convergent numerical method was devised by Weber and Saalfeld (1954) for light loading, but unfortunately it will not work in the important range of loading.

The first significant results for practical loads were obtained by Grubin (1949) using an inspired simplification; the analysis is described in some detail below. Petrusevich (1951) produced three solutions by a trial-and-error method which has not been published; the general nature of the results appear to be correct, but this work is put into some doubt by its main conclusion — a formula which predicts that the film thickness increases with the applied load. A paper by Poritsky (1952) contains a number of valuable observations on the problem, but no solutions. Two of these observations are very important:

(1) The integrated form of Reynolds equation is

$$\frac{dp}{dx} = 12\eta u \left[\frac{h - h_m}{h^3} \right] \qquad (6.4)$$

Over most of the width of the contact the pressure is so high that the viscosity is orders of magnitude bigger than its atmospheric value, so if dp/dx is to have realistic values, $h - h_m$ must be very small, in fact approximately zero. In other words, the *film thickness must be constant over most of the high pressure zone.* Another important feature of the oil film geometry can be determined by considering the outlet region. Since in high load cases the Hertzian load represents a close approximation to the actual load, the oil-film boundaries will diverge comparatively rapidly beyond the thin film zone. Thus if the outlet boundary condition for the pressure curve discussed earlier is applied, the pressure curve must terminate very near to the end of this zone. Consequently, large pressure gradients must exist near the end of the zone to reduce the pressure to the ambient value. The integrated form of Reynolds' equation shows that large pressure gradients at comparatively low pressures, and hence low viscosities, can be achieved only by a reduction in the film thickness. Thus a *significant local reduction in the film thickness will occur near the end of the thin film zone.*

(2) When the load is large and the speed not very high, the film thickness will be small compared even with the local elastic displacements. Therefore, except near the edges of the zone, the pressure distribution must be close to the Hertzian distribution for dry contact. On the other hand if the load is small or the speed very high, the film thickness will be large compared with the local deformation and the pressure distribution can be expected to be more like that for rigid cylinders.

Dimensional Analysis

The calculations described below are laborious, so economy can be effected by examining the nature and range of the variables involved. The requirements of a solution are the pressure distribution and roller geometry—or film shape—for a specified load and speed. The most important practical feature of the solution is the minimum film thickness to be expected, and its relation to the surface finish of the solids. The imposed variables in the isothermal problem are:

R the effective radius of the roller pair.
E' the effective elastic modulus of the roller pair.
η_0, α the viscous properties of the lubricant.
w, u the external variables, load per unit width and speed.
h is the unknown film thickness.

The seven independent variables have dimensions as follows:

$$
\begin{array}{ccccccc}
h & R & E' & \eta_0 & \alpha & w & u \\[2mm]
L & L & \dfrac{M}{LT^2} & \dfrac{M}{LT} & \dfrac{LT^2}{M} & \dfrac{M}{T^2} & \dfrac{L}{T}
\end{array}
$$

h is therefore governed by three dimensionless ratios. A convenient set is

$$
\frac{h}{R} = f\left(\frac{w}{E'R} , \; \frac{\eta_0 u}{E'R} , \; \alpha E' \right)
$$

These ratios will be denoted by H, W, U and G. The values of these dimensionless groups are looked at below:

The load parameter:

$$
W = \frac{w}{E'R}
$$

A value of 3×10^{-4} corresponds to a maximum Hertzian pressure of about 1·5 GPa (100 tons/in²) on steel; 3×10^{-5} corresponds to about 0·5 GPa (30 tons/in²).

The speed parameter:

$$
U = \frac{\eta_0 u}{E'R}
$$

It will be seen later that this is the most influential variable, so a wide range of values (5 orders of magnitude) has been investigated: 10^{-8}–10^{-13}. This range overlaps both ends of the practical range.

The materials parameter:

$$G = \alpha E'$$

All the published values of α for lubricants lie in a narrow range, Likewise E', for metals of any rate, does not vary very much. So in practice the range of $\alpha E'$ is small, unless the contacting solids are non-metallic.

Grubin's Theory

In a lengthy paper Grubin examined in detail many aspects of the elasto-hydrodynamic problem. Only a small part of his analysis, the derivation of a formula for film thickness, will be reproduced here. The derivation rests on two simplifying assumptions; they are (1) that the deformed shape of the cylinders will be the same as that in a dry contact and (2) that a high pressure is developed in the entry region to the Hertzian zone. The geometry, in terms of an equivalent elastic cylinder and a rigid plane, is shown in Fig. 4.1.

The Hertzian displacement outside the contact zone is given by

$$H - H_0 = \frac{h - h_0}{R}$$

$$= \frac{4W}{\pi} [X(X^2 - 1)^{1/2} - \ln (X + [X^2 - 1]^{1/2})]$$

where $X = x/b$ and W is the load parameter defined above. In terms of the reduced pressure, the integrated form of the Reynolds equation is

$$\frac{dq}{dx} = 12\eta_0 u \left[\frac{h - h_0}{h^3} \right]$$

Writing $Q = q/E'$ and remembering that $b/R = 4(W/2\pi)^{1/2}$, this becomes in dimensionless form

$$\frac{dQ}{dX} = 48 \left(\frac{W}{2\pi} \right)^{1/2} U \frac{H - H_0}{H^3}$$

The pressure developed at the inlet edge of the Hertzian zone will be therefore

$$Q_{X=-1} = 48 \left(\frac{W}{2\pi}\right)^{1/2} U \int_{-\infty}^{-1} \left(\frac{H - H_0}{H^3}\right) dX$$

Grubin evaluated this integral numerically for a range of values of H_0 and found an expression which gave a good fit over the range of practical importance. Actually his variables were slightly different from those used here, such that

$$\int_{-\infty}^{-1} \left(\frac{H - H_0}{H^3}\right) dX = \left(\frac{\pi}{2W}\right)^2 \times \text{Grubin's integral.}$$

Grubin's integral is fitted closely by

$$0 \cdot 0986 \left(\frac{\pi H_0}{2W}\right)^{-11/8}$$

so

$$Q_{X=-1} = 48 \left(\frac{W}{2\pi}\right)^{1/2} U \left(\frac{\pi}{2W}\right)^2 \times 0 \cdot 0986 \left(\frac{\pi H_0}{2W}\right)^{-11/8} \quad (6.5)$$

Now Grubin argued that the pressure must reach a significant fraction of the Hertzian maximum at $X = -1$, which for practical contact loads would be so high that $\exp(-\alpha p) \ll 1$, so $q \approx 1/\alpha$ (see eqn. (6.3)), or in the dimensionless terms $Q_{X=-1} = 1/G$. Putting this into (6.5) and transposing gives an expression for H_0, the dimensionless film thickness:

$$H_0 = \frac{1 \cdot 95 (GU)^{8/11}}{W^{1/11}} \quad (6.6)$$

There are of course features of the contact mechanism which do not emerge from this simple analysis, but it will be seen later that values of film thickness predicted by (6.6) are remarkably close to those calculated by the more accurate method described below and to those found experimentally.

A Numerical Solution

Three basic numerical processes have been used to obtain the results which will be described in the next chapter. These are:

(1) The integration of Reynolds' equation to give the pressure distribution for a known geometry.

(2) The inverse solution of the Reynolds equation, yielding the geometry which would engender a specified pressure distribution.

(3) The calculation of surface displacements.

In the hydrodynamic part of the calculation, process (1) is used in the long inlet sweep where the pressures are relatively low. At high pressures this process is not so useful because it involves very large and very small quantities; in this region, and on the outlet side, process (2) is used. The overall computation consists essentially of a rapidly convergent iteration over the inlet side up to fairly high pressures, and successive modification of the remainder of the pressure curve to bring the results of (2) and (3) into agreement.

The calculation is not an easy one and the time taken depends on the experience of the operator. A fairly accurate film thickness can be found in two or three cycles, but the full solution may take a dozen cycles. Some general features of the calculations are:

(1) In medium–high load/low–medium speed cases, the pressure curve is close to Hertzian over much of the zone width. Such cases are described as near-Hertzian.

(2) In near-Hertzian cases, the Reynolds equation demands a parallel film over most of the zone. Thus, because of the logarithmic nature of the elastic displacements, the net addition of load to the Hertzian distribution at either side must be small. So on the inlet side, the pressure curve must come inside the Hertzian curve to balance the inlet sweep. Similarly, on the outlet side there must be a positive addition to the Hertzian curve as well as the negative addition required to produce the constriction in the film.

Some Details of the Calculation

(1) The numerical integration of the Reynolds equation is quite straightforward. For an incompressible lubricant all the terms in the integrand for reduced pressure are known, and Simpson's rule can be used. On the other hand, for a compressible fluid the density, which depends on pressure, appears in the integrand.

$$\frac{dq}{dx} = 12\eta_0 u \left(1 - \frac{\varrho_m h_m}{\varrho h}\right) \Big/ h^2$$

In this case the first three terms in a Taylor expansion are used in a step-by-step numerical integration:

$$q_{n+1} \approx q_n + \Delta x \left(\frac{dq}{dx}\right)_n + \frac{(\Delta x)^2}{2} \left(\frac{d^2 q}{dx^2}\right)_n$$

dq/dx is given above and $d^2 q/dx^2$ can be written as,

$$\frac{d^2 q}{dx^2} = \frac{12\eta_0 u}{h^2} \left[\frac{1}{h}\frac{dh}{dx}(1 - 3r) + \frac{1}{\varrho}\frac{d\varrho}{dx}(1 - r)\right]$$

where

$$r = \left(1 - \frac{\varrho_m h_m}{\varrho h}\right)$$

ϱ is expressed in terms of p, and $d\varrho/dx$ replaced by $d\varrho/dp\,dp/dx$.

(2) The inverse solution of the Reynolds equation is obtained as follows. For an incompressible fluid eqn. (2.8) yields on differentiation

$$h^3 \frac{d}{dx}\left(\frac{1}{\eta}\frac{dp}{dx}\right) - \frac{dh}{dx}\left(12u - \frac{3h^2}{\eta}\frac{dp}{dx}\right) = 0 \qquad (6.7)$$

In general, for films bounded by continuous solids, two points can be located on the pressure curve where

$$\frac{d}{dx}\left(\frac{1}{\eta}\frac{dp}{dx}\right) = 0 \qquad (6.8)$$

One of these points is on the inlet pressure sweep and the other near the outlet. In the special case of constant viscosity they are the points of inflexion in the pressure curve; for viscosity which varies exponentially with pressure they are the points of inflection in the reduced pressure curve. When (6.8) is satisfied, eqn. (6.7) reduces to

$$\frac{dh}{dx}\left(12u - \frac{3h^2}{\eta}\frac{dp}{dx}\right) = 0 \qquad (6.9)$$

Solutions to (6.9) are

$$\left.\begin{array}{cc} \dfrac{dh}{dx} = 0 & a \\[2mm] \dfrac{dp}{dx} = \dfrac{4\eta u}{h^2} & b \end{array}\right\} \qquad (6.10)$$

At the outlet end of the pressure curve the gradient is negative and so the solution is $dh/dx = 0$, the point of minimum film thickness. At inlet where the film is convergent $dh/dx \neq 0$, so (6.10) gives $dp/dx = 4\eta u/h^2$. Thus for known speed and viscosity the film thickness at the point where (6.8) applies can be found for any given pressure curve. Using suffix a for this point,

$$h_a = \left(\frac{4\eta_a u}{\left(\dfrac{dp}{dx}\right)_a}\right)^{1/2}$$

Once h_a has been found the entire film shape corresponding to the given pressure curve can be calculated from the integrated form of the Reynolds equation (2.10). Substituting (6.10b) into (2.10) for the point a gives at once

$$h_m = \tfrac{2}{3} h_a$$

At other points h can be found by solving the cubic equation in h obtained by rearranging (2.10)

$$K\bar{h}^3 - \bar{h} + 1 = 0 \qquad (6.11)$$

where

$$K = \frac{h_m^2}{12\eta u} \frac{dp}{dx} \quad \text{and} \quad \bar{h} = \frac{h}{h_m}$$

At any point on the inlet pressure sweep up to the maximum pressure K is positive and (6.11) presents one negative and two positive roots (the positive roots coincide at the point a). It is obvious which is the appropriate positive value of h. Between the maximum pressure and outlet, K is negative. In this region eqn. (6.11) has only one real root, which is positive and gives the required film thickness. Figure 6.1 shows the positive real roots obtained from the theoretical pressure curve for a rigid cylinder rolling on a plane.

The only tricky feature of this inverse solution is the location of the point on the inlet side where (6.8) is satisfied; numerically this involves finding the zero of the second differences of a list of pressures. It is found in practice that repeated smoothing of the pressures and their first differences facilitates the accurate location of the point.

The inclusion of compressibility in the calculation makes very little difference. The Reynolds equation with variable fluid density is

$$\frac{d}{dx}\left(\frac{\varrho h^3}{\eta} \frac{dp}{dx}\right) = 12u \frac{d}{dx}(\varrho h)$$

If the variables h and η are replaced by ϱh and $\varrho^2 \eta$ the calculation is not substantially altered.

(3) The surface displacements are calculated by dividing the pressure curve into suitable blocks, not of equal size, and representing each block by appropriate values of the constants A_n described in Chapter 5. The first three terms in the polynomial are used and the origin of coordinates taken at the centre of each block in turn. Writing $X = x/b$, $l = -s_1/b = s_2/b$ where b is

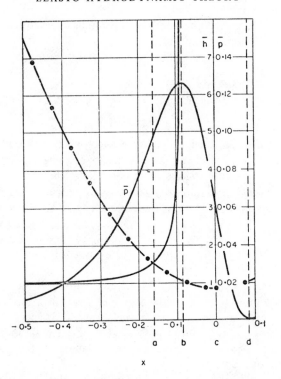

FIG. 6.1. Positive roots $\bar{h}$ obtained from Reynolds equation for the theoretical pressure distribution based on constant viscosity and rigid cylinders. ● profile of cylinder.

[Reproduced from the *Journal of Mechanical Engineering Science*, Vol. 1, No. 1, pp. 6–15 (1959) by kind permission of the Institution of Mechanical Engineers.]

half the Hertzian contact width, the coefficients in the displacements become

$$F_0 = 2\{(X - l)\ln|X - l| - (X + l)\ln|X + l|\}$$

$$F_1 = (X^2 - l^2)\ln|X - l| - (X^2 - l^2)\ln|X + l| + 2lX$$

$$F_2 = \tfrac{2}{3}\{(X^3 - l^3)\ln|X - l| - (X^3 + l^3)\ln|X + l| + 2lX^2\}$$

When $X \gg l$, difficulty arises in calculating the coefficients in this form because small differences are involved; however, for large values of X/l, the logarithm terms can be expanded and the coefficients calculated in the form

$$F_0 = -2l\left[\ln |X^2 - l^2| + 2\left\{1 + \frac{1}{3}\left(\frac{l}{X}\right)^2 + \frac{1}{5}\left(\frac{l}{X}\right)^4 + \cdots\right\}\right)$$

$$F_1 = 4l^2 \frac{l}{X}\left\{\frac{1}{3} + \frac{1}{15}\left(\frac{l}{X}\right)^2 + \frac{1}{35}\left(\frac{l}{X}\right)^4 + \cdots\right\}$$

$$F_2 = -\frac{2}{3}l^3\left[\ln |X^2 - l^2| + 2\left\{\frac{1}{3} + \frac{1}{5}\left(\frac{l}{X}\right)^2 + \frac{1}{7}\left(\frac{l}{X}\right)^4 + \cdots\right\}\right]$$

In dimensionless form, the displacement is

$$V = \frac{v}{R} = \frac{8P_0^{\,2}}{\pi} \sum AF + \text{constant} \qquad (6.12)$$

In those cases where the pressure curve is close to Hertzian, the displacements calculated are those arising from the difference between the actual pressure curve and the Hertzian curve; these are then added to the Hertzian form of deformation. Any linear correction of the form $Ax + B$ can be added to the displacements arbitrarily. The constant term B is inherent in the integration constant on (6.12) and the term Ax is equivalent to a shift of the pressure along the surface of the cylinder. The film thickness is

$$h = h_0 + \frac{x^2}{2R} + v$$

If we move the centre-line of the cylinders a distance c relative to the pressure distribution the film thickness becomes

$$h' = h_0 + \frac{(x - c)^2}{2R} + v$$

The change in film thickness is $-cx/R +$ constant. Therefore a centre-line shift of c produces a linear change in the film thickness or, in other words, a change in slope of the datum of $-c/R$.

CHAPTER 7

THEORETICAL RESULTS

MOST of the results presented in this chapter will be in terms of the dimensionless parameters which have been shown to represent the problem. They are concerned primarily with the ways in which the external variables, load, speed and material properties, influence the distribution of pressure between the solids and the thickness of the film of oil separating them. The values of the dimensionless groups have been chosen to cover, where .necessary, the range likely to be encountered in engineering practice. The first few results, however, are in dimensional terms and for conditions outside the usual practical range, being relevant to a particular experiment which is briefly described in the next chapter; they are included here because they illustrate a number of important points. The constants in these calculations are:

$$R = 2 \text{ m (78 in)}, \quad u = 1 \text{ m/s}, \quad \eta_0 = 0.137 \text{ Pas}$$

$$E = 1.08 \times 10^{11} \text{ N/m}^2 \text{ (7000 ton /in}^2\text{)}, \quad \sigma = 0.3$$

The first of these preliminary results is shown in Fig. 7.1, which demonstrates the effects of viscosity variation and elastic deformation on the pressure distribution and film shape, for a particular centre-line film thickness. The notable feature of this result is the vast combined influence of these two additions to the simple theory compared with their modest separate effects. All the results presented from now on include both effects. The change in form of the pressure curve as the load is increased is shown in Fig. 7.2. The movement towards a Hertzian pressure distribution is plain to see. This figure also shows the film shape for each load. The constriction in the oil film at the outlet end is

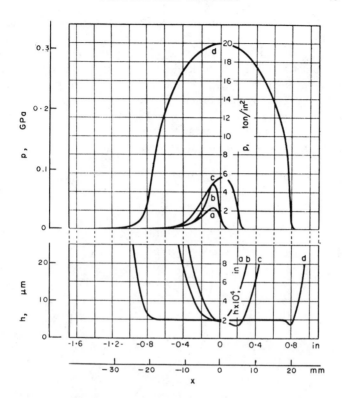

FIG. 7.1. Pressure distributions and film shapes for the same centre-line film thickness. (a) Constant viscosity, rigid cylinders. (b) Pressure-dependent viscosity, rigid cylinders. (c) Constant viscosity, elastic cylinders. (d) Pressure-dependent viscosity, elastic cylinders.

[Reproduced from the *Journal of Mechanical Engineering Science*, Vol. 1, No. 1, pp. 6–15 (1959) by kind permission of the Institution of Mechanical Engineers.]

quite substantial (the minimum thickness is about three-quarters of the long parallel thickness). Striking also is the small variation of film thickness with load; this is probably the most important result of elasto-hydrodynamic theory and is shown in a different form in Fig. 7.3. In these preliminary calculations the viscosity–pressure variation employed is shown in Fig. 7.4; this curve refers to a particular mineral oil and is based on figures supplied by Thornton Research Centre. In all the other calculations the exponential viscosity–pressure relationship is used, and

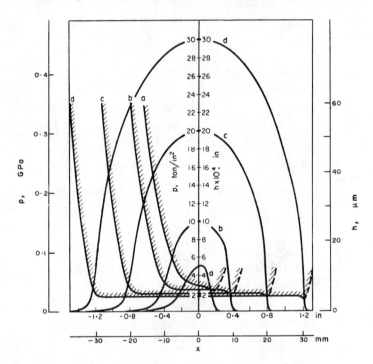

FIG. 7.2. Pressure distributions and film shapes with pressure-dependent viscosity and elastic cylinders.

[Reproduced from the *Journal of Mechanical Engineering Science*, Vol. 1, No. 1, pp. 6–15 (1959) by kind permission of the Institution of Mechanical Engineers.]

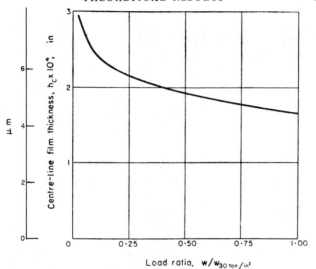

FIG. 7.3. Variation of centre-line film thickness with load.
[Reproduced from the *Journal of Mechanical Engineering Science*,
Vol. 1, No. 1, pp. 6–15 (1959) by kind permission of the Institu-
tion of Mechanical Engineers.]

the values of the dimensionless parameters in which the results are
presented correspond to engineering reality.† Some guide to the
practical significance of the parameters is given in the table below.

$W = 3 \times 10^{-5}$	About 0·5 GPa (30 tons/in²) Hertzian maximum pressure on steel
$W = 3 \times 10^{-4}$	About 1·5 GPa (100 tons/in²) Hertzian maximum pressure on steel
$U = 10^{-11}$	About 1 m/s with a 0·1 Pas oil lubricating rollers with $R = 40$ mm.
$G = 5000$	Materials: steel and mineral oil
$G = 2500$	Materials: bronze and mineral oil

† All except the preliminary results were obtained with the help of the
Ferranti Pegasus installation LUCIFER in the Computing Laboratory of
Leeds University.

We see at once in Figs. 7.5 and 7.6 a striking difference in the pressure distributions from those in the earlier figures, viz. the pressure peak on the outlet side. This peak in the isothermal solution is in agreement with the predictions of Grubin and the calculations of Petrusevich; such peaks are absent from Fig. 7.2 because the value of G there is low and that of U very low, a condition which would not produce a peak, as has been noted

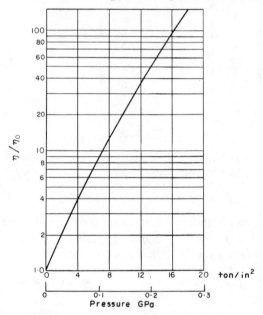

FIG. 7.4. Variation of viscosity with pressure. $\eta_0 = 0.137$ Pas
[Reproduced from the *Journal of Mechanical Engineering Science*, Vol. 1, No. 1, pp. 6–15 (1959) by kind permission of the Institution of Mechanical Engineers.]

also by Archard and Gair and Hirst. The other important features of the pressure curves in Figs. 7.5 and 7.6 are the dependence of the height of the peak on G and its near-independence of W, for an incompressible lubricant. The film thickness is again seen to be little affected by the load, but is quite sharply dependent on the materials parameter G. However, the range of

G in practice is small, for metallic contacts at any rate, so it appears that the film thickness is almost entirely dependent upon the speed parameter U. The pressure distribution of course will be much influenced by the load.

The combination of high load and fairly low speed embodied in Fig. 7.6 represents an extreme practical condition and constitutes a severe test of the likelihood of effective hydrodynamic lubrication. The predicted film thickness is $2 \times 10^{-5} \times$ (the effective radius); this appears to uphold the possibility of hydrodynamic lubrication if the surface finish is of the highest quality.

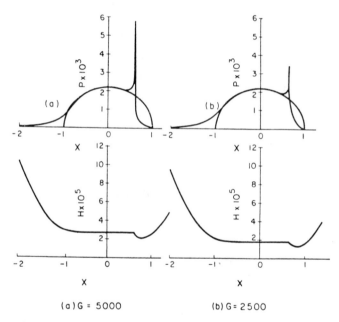

FIG. 7.5. Pressure distributions and film shapes. $W = 3 \times 10^{-5}$. $U = 10^{-11}$. (a) $G = 5000$. (b) $G = 2500$.

[Reproduced from the *Journal of Mechanical Engineering Science*, Vol. 2, No. 3, pp. 188–194 (1960) by kind permission of the Institution of Mechanical Engineers.]

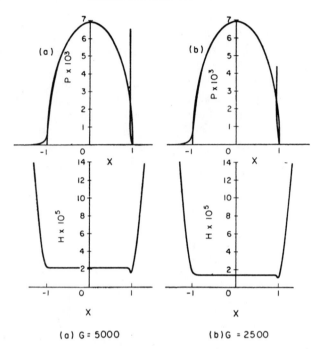

(a) G = 5000   (b) G = 2500

FIG. 7.6. Pressure distributions and film shapes. $W = 3 \times 10^{-4}$. $U = 10^{-11}$. (a) $G = 5000$. (b) $G = 2500$.

[Reproduced from the *Journal of Mechanical Engineering Science*, Vol. 2, No. 3, pp. 188–194 (1960) by kind permission of the Institution of Mechanical Engineers.]

Speed Effects

We turn now to the most important variable in the isothermal analysis – speed; or more accurately the product of speed and inlet viscosity. This quantity is plotted in the dimensionless form $U = \eta_0 u / E'R$. The variation of minimum film thickness with U is shown in Fig. 7.7; from this line it can be deduced that $H_{min} \propto U^{0.7}$ in this range. For comparison the film thickness indicated by the classical theory is also shown. These lines converge at very high speed where the effects of elasticity and viscosity-increase become less important, because the film thickness is large and the pressure relatively low for a given load.

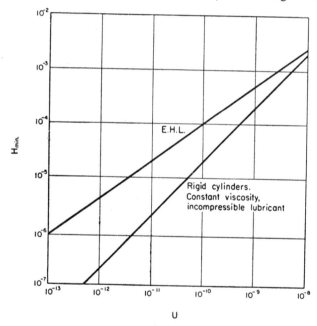

FIG. 7.7. Variation of film thickness with speed. $W = 3 \times 10^{-5}$, $G = 5000$. [Reproduced by kind permission from the *Proceedings of the Institution of Mechanical Engineers Symposium on Fatigue in Rolling Contact*, 1963.]

The changes of detail with speed at constant load are illustrated by the next two figures. Figure 7.8 shows the spectacular changes in the pressure distribution; the speed parameter increases by a factor of 10 from one curve to the next. This dia-

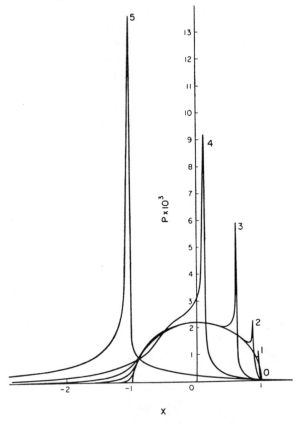

FIG. 7.8. Pressure distributions for an incompressible lubricant. $W = 3 \times 10^{-5}$, $G = 5000$. $U = (0)$ 0 (dry contact), (1) 10^{-13}, (2) 10^{-12}, (3) 10^{-11}, (4) 10^{-10}, (5) 10^{-9}.

[Reproduced from the *Journal of Mechanical Engineering Science*, Vol. 4, No. 2, pp. 121–6 (1962) by kind permission of the Institution of Mechanical Engineers.]

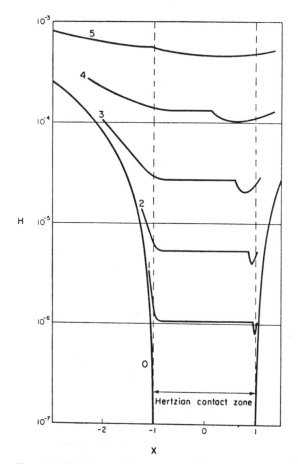

Fig. 7.9. Film shapes for an incompressible lubricant. $W = 3 \times 10^{-5}$, $G = 5000$. $U = (0)\ 0$ (dry contact), (1) 10^{-13}, (2) 10^{-12}, (3) 10^{-11}, (4) 10^{-10}, (5) 10^{-9}.

[Reproduced from the *Journal of Mechanical Engineering Science*, Vol. 4, No. 2, pp. 121–6 (1962) by kind permission of the Institution of Mechanical Engineers.]

gram shows clearly how the theoretical pressure departs from Hertzian as the speed increases, leading to maximum values far in excess of the Hertzian maximum. The shapes of the fluid films corresponding to these pressure curves are shown in Fig. 7.9. Owing to the considerable change in film thickness over the speed range examined, a logarithmic plot is presented. The envelope of the film shapes, labelled (0) in the figure, is the shape of the deformed cylinder in dry contact; as the speed is reduced the film shape settles towards this Hertzian contour. An essential feature of the film shapes is the constriction at the outlet end. With increasing speed this constriction occupies an increasing proportion of the Hertzian contact zone; indeed at the highest speed in this range it commences before the inlet side of the Hertzian zone is reached. In all cases the minimum film thickness is found to be about three-quarters of the thickness at the point of maximum pressure.

From the analysis so far the speed parameter U emerges as the dominant independent variable. The influence of the materials parameter G encountered in practice is relatively small.

Effects of Lubricant Compressibility

The compressibility of the lubricant has not so far been included in the analysis; but in view of the high pressures involved in the practical applications where this analysis is appropriate, and in view of the rather fantastic nature of the pressure distributions in Fig. 7.8, it seems worth while to find out whether its influence is significant. It was shown in the last chapter that, in principle, it is not difficult to modify the theory to take account of compressibility.

The variation of density with pressure is roughly linear at low pressure, but the rate of increase of density falls away at high pressure. The limit of the compression of mineral oils is about 25 per cent (Grubin, 1949), giving a maximum density increase of about 33 per cent. Figures supplied by Thornton Research Centre for a mineral oil are plotted in Fig. 7.10. It will be seen that these fit closely to the expression

$$\frac{\rho}{\rho_0} = 1 + \frac{0 \cdot 6p}{1 + 1 \cdot 7p}$$

where p is in GPa; this gives a maximum density increase of about 33 per cent. Including compressibility in the analysis introduces another variable, so the dimensional analysis is altered;

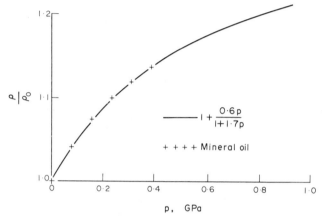

FIG. 7.10. Density–pressure relationship.
[Reproduced from the *Journal of Mechanical Engineering Science*, Vol. 4, No. 2, pp. 121–6 (1962) by kind permission of the Institution of Mechanical Engineers.]

subsequent results apply only to steel rollers for this particular rate of compressibility.

The most important effect of compressibility is on the peak in the pressure distribution. Comparison of Fig. 7.11 and 7.8 shows that in all cases the peak is moved downstream and is reduced in height; the reduction is particularly drastic at high speeds. An interesting change is in the envelope of the pressure curves. At the highest speeds shown in Fig. 7.11 ($U = 10^{-8\frac{1}{2}}$ and 10^{-8}, which are well outside the practical range) the pressure distributions are indistinguishable from those calculated by rigid cylinder theory. The effect of load on the pressure distribution

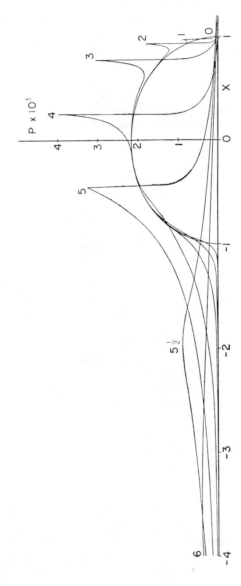

FIG. 7.11. Pressure distributions for a compressible lubricant. $W = 3 \times 10^{-5}$, $G = 5000$. $U = (0)$ 0 (dry contact), (1) 10^{-13}, (2) 10^{-12}, (3) 10^{-11}, (4) 10^{-10}, (5) 10^{-9}, ($5\frac{1}{2}$) $10^{-8\frac{1}{2}}$, (6) 10^{-8}. [Reproduced by kind permission from the *Proceedings of the Institution of Mechanical Engineers Symposium on Fatigue in Rolling Contact*, 1963.]

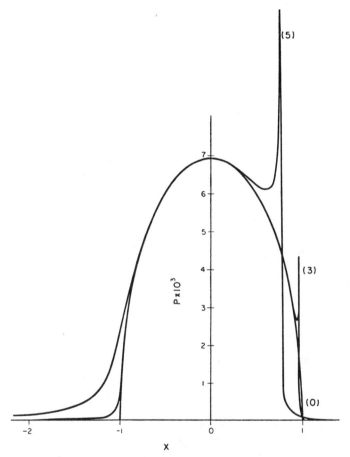

FIG. 7.12. Pressure distributions for a compressible lubricant. $W = 3 \times 10^{-4}$, $G = 5000$. $U = (0)$ 0 (dry contact), (3) 10^{-11}, (5) 10^{-9}.

[Reproduced by kind permission from the *Proceedings of the Institution of Mechanical Engineers Symposium on Fatigue in Rolling Contact*, 1963.]

is demonstrated in Fig. 7.12, where the load is ten times that in Fig. 7.11. The form is unchanged, but evidently the effect on the shape (apart from scale) of a tenfold increase in load is much the same as a reduction of two orders of magnitude in the speed parameter U.

The general form of the film shape is not altered by compressibility, but there are changes in detail. Figure 7.13 shows the shapes for compressible and incompressible lubricants with $U = 10^{-11}$. This result is typical: (a) the minimum film thickness is not significantly changed, (b) the film which is parallel with an incompressible lubricant becomes a curved channel in which the product of density and film thickness remains sensibly constant and (c) the fairly sharp corner associated with the pressure peak is removed. A result of (a) and (b) is that the minimum film thickness is no longer a fixed 25 per cent less than that under the Hertzian maximum pressure; the difference now depends on the compressibility and the magnitude of the pressure. The overall picture is not much altered by the inclusion of variation of lubricant density in the analysis, but the changes in the details just described do make the solutions more acceptable intuitively.

Friction Force

The surface traction in pure rolling due to the viscous stresses on the surface can be evaluated as follows: in pure rolling, the force per unit width of roller, F_R, is given by

$$2F_R = \int_i^0 h\, \frac{\partial p}{\partial x}\, \mathrm{d}x$$

It is assumed throughout the analysis that p varies only with x, and so $\partial p/\partial x$ can be written $\mathrm{d}p/\mathrm{d}x$, so

$$2F_R = \int_i^0 h\, \mathrm{d}p$$

This can easily be evaluated numerically from the results described earlier. It is found that F_R is independent of load over

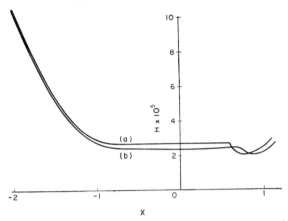

FIG. 7.13. Film shapes. $W = 3 \times 10^{-5}$, $G = 5000$, $U = 10^{-11}$.
(a) Incompressible lubricant. (b) Compressible lubricant.
[Reproduced from the *Journal of Mechanical Engineering Science*,
Vol. 4, No. 2, pp. 121–6 (1962) by kind permission of the Institution of Mechanical Engineers.]

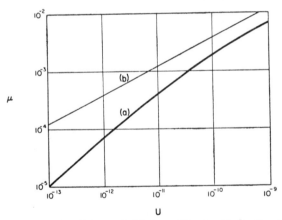

FIG. 7.14. Coefficient of friction. $W = 3 \times 10^{-5}$, $G = 5000$.
(a) Elasto-hydrodynamic theory. (b) Rigid rollers; isoviscous,
incompressible lubricant.

[Reproduced from the *Journal of Mechanical Engineering Science*,
Vol. 4, No. 2, pp. 121–6 (1962) by kind permission of the Institution of Mechanical Engineers.]

the range examined, and varies with $\eta_0 u$ at about the same rate as does the film thickness. To a first approximation, therefore, the friction force in pure rolling is simply proportional to the film thickness. The variation of the friction force with speed is shown in Fig. 7.14 in the form of a coefficient of friction, F_R/w, plotted against the speed parameter U. It is compared with the corresponding figure given by the simple theory; as expected, the two curves converge at high speed.

A detailed examination of the friction force in both rolling and sliding contacts will be found in Chapter 10.

Stresses in the Rollers

The stresses in the solids are engendered effectively by the normal lubricant pressure only. The contribution of the tangential viscous traction is negligible. Several stress fields have

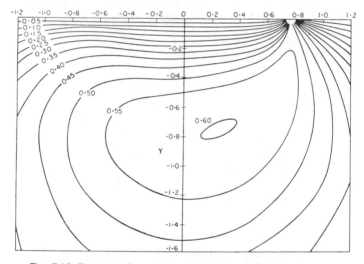

FIG. 7.15. Contours of maximum principal stress difference/maximum Hertzian pressure. $W = 3 \times 10^{-5}$, $G = 5000$, $U = 10^{-11}$. [Reproduced by kind permission from the *Proceedings of the Institution of Mechanical Engineers Symposium on Fatigue in Rolling Contact*, 1963.]

been calculated and are presented in some detail elsewhere (Dowson, Higginson and Whitaker, 1963). One result is given in Fig. 7.15 in the form of contours of maximum principal stress difference. It is found that as the speed parameter increases the large shear stresses are drawn towards the surface. Apart from this change of location, however, the ranges of shear stress in the solids are not much affected by the presence of a lubricant. Indeed, at really high loads the stress picture is essenitally Hertzian at any realistic value of the speed parameter.

Summary of Theoretical Results

1. For a given load and rolling speed, over the range which is important in current practice, the minimum film thickness is very much greater than the simple theory would indicate.

2. In the range of conditions where elastic deformation is important, film thickness is only slightly dependent on load.

3. The influence on the film thickness of the materials parameter G is almost as great as that of the speed parameter U, but the range of G in practice is small. So U emerges as the dominant variable.

4. As the load increases and/or (speed × viscosity) decreases the pressure distribution tends from the hydrodynamic distribution for rigid cylinders towards the semi-elliptical Hertzian distribution for dry contact of the cylinders.

5. For the conditions and materials encountered in engineering practice there is usually a sharp secondary peak on the outlet side of the pressure distribution.

6. In pure rolling the friction force is independent of load, and varies with U at the same rate as does the film thickness.

7. At high loads the stress field in the solids is essentially Hertzian.

Formula for Film Thickness

The method described above to obtain the solution to a rolling-contact lubrication problem is too cumbersome to be used by a designer. However, the feature of the solution which is the designer's prime concern is the minimum film thickness. It has been found (Dowson and Higginson, 1961) that the minimum film thickness over the whole range of theoretical solutions can be fairly accurately represented by the formula

$$H^* = \frac{1 \cdot 6 G^{0 \cdot 6} U^{0 \cdot 7}}{W^{0 \cdot 13}} \qquad (7.1)$$

Figure 7.16 shows the values of H_{min} obtained from a wide range of theoretical solutions plotted against H^*. The agreement is close. Also the formula is in complete accord with the results of Archard, Gair and Hirst. It is interesting to compare formula (7.1) with Grubin's, which is

$$H = \frac{1 \cdot 95 (GU)^{0 \cdot 73}}{W^{0 \cdot 091}}$$

The discrepancy between the two is never more than about 20 per cent. It is interesting also to write (7.1) in full in dimensional terms.

$$h = \frac{1 \cdot 6 \alpha^{0 \cdot 6} (\eta_0 u)^{0 \cdot 7} (E')^{0 \cdot 03} R^{0 \cdot 43}}{w^{0 \cdot 13}} \qquad (7.2)$$

It appears that not only is h only slightly dependent on the load w, but it is virtually independent of the elastic modulus E'. This theoretical result is confirmed by Crook's experiments with a glass disk rolling on a steel disk, where the film thickness was found to be much the same as between steel disks under the same external conditions (see Chapter 9). Of course, the zone width and pressure distribution are very dependent on the elastic modulus of the solids.

Finally the limited range of application of this formula must
be emphasized. It can only be applied in conditions corresponding to those of the full-scale computations, viz. metals in contact
under high loads and lubricated by a fluid whose viscosity–
pressure relationship resembles that of a mineral oil. For a constant viscosity oil ($\alpha = 0$), for instance, the formula predicts zero
film thickness, which is nonsense.

Blok (1959) and later Koets (1962) have surveyed the work
of most of the contributors to the subject of rolling contact
lubrication, particularly the theoretical work. Using a different
set of dimensionless groups from those used in this monograph,
they have reconciled the film thickness calculations of Grubin

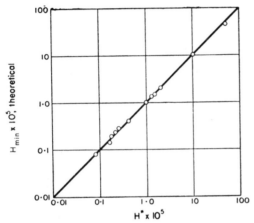

FIG. 7.16. Comparison of theoretical $H_{\min}$ with H^*.
[Reproduced from *Engineering* (4 August 1961) by kind permission of the Editor.]

and Archand, Gair and Hirst and the authors at high loads with
those of Weber and Saalfeld at low loads and the original Martin
result for rigid cylinders. Koets's dimensionless groups are, in
terms of the groups used by the authors,

$$T = \frac{H}{(2U)^{1/2}} : M = \frac{W}{(2U)^{1/2}} : L = G(2U)^{1/4}$$

It will be noted that Koets expresses the dimensionless film thickness T in terms of only two other quantities, M and L.

Martin's result, which can be applied when the load is very low, is

$$TM = 2 \cdot 45$$

or, in terms of our groups

$$H = 4 \cdot 9 \, \frac{U}{W}$$

This is the dimensionless equivalent of eqn. (4.1). The film thickness is directly proportional to (speed × viscosity) and inversely proportional to load. This result is in sharp contrast to the results of elasto-hydrodynamic theory represented by formula (7.1).

Two comprehensive diagrams from the paper by Koets are reproduced without significant alteration in Figs. 7.17 and 7.18. From the first of these Koets concludes "The combination of the results of Weber and Saalfeld and Dowson and Higginson describes the whole practical range of elasto-hydrodynamic lubrication fairly well", and on the strength of this draws the second as a representation of the entire isothermal theory. In this diagram the curves showing film thicknesses given by elasto-hydrodynamic theory tend assymptotically towards the Martin result.

A similar diagram, plotted in terms of the dimensionless groups employed by the authors, has been presented by Dowson and Whitaker (1964). The diagram which is reproduced here as Fig. 7.19, shows contours of H for a wide range of U and W. The curves in the "rigid" region shown in Fig. 7.19 are plotted directly from the Martin formula for rigid cylinders lubricated by an isoviscous lubricant ($H = 4 \cdot 9 U/W$).

The contours shown in the "elastic" region have been calculated from the authors' elasto-hydrodynamic film thickness formula (7.1); the value of the materials parameter G being restricted to 5000.

Dowson and Whitaker noted that the transition from the Martin condition to the full elasto-hydrodynamic situation was

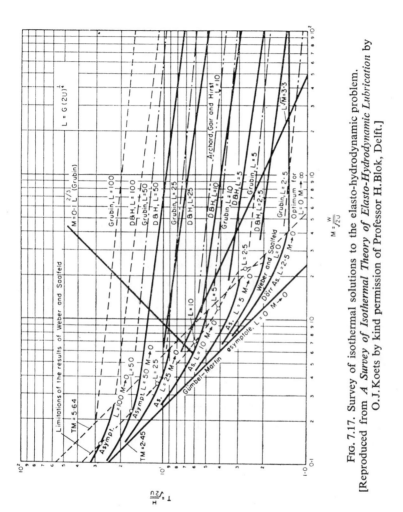

FIG. 7.17. Survey of isothermal solutions to the elasto-hydrodynamic problem.
[Reproduced from *A Survey of Isothermal Theory of Elasto-Hydrodynamic Lubrication* by
O.J.Koets by kind permission of Professor H.Blok, Delft.]

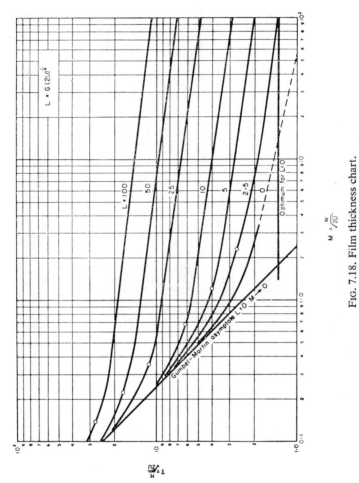

Fig. 7.18. Film thickness chart.

[Reproduced from *A Survey of Isothermal Theory of Elasto-Hydrodynamic Lubrication* by O.J.Koets by kind permission of Professor H.Blok, Delft.]

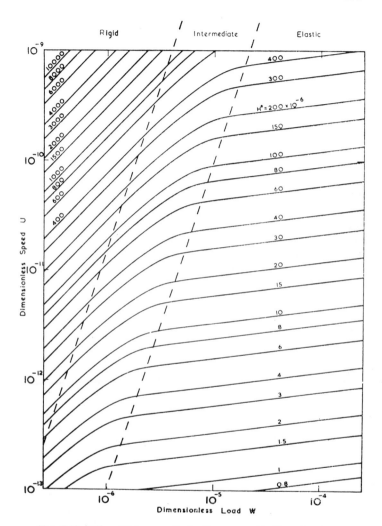

Fig. 7.19. Film thickness chart. Contours of $H^* = h_{min}/R$, $G = 5000$.
[Published by kind permission of the *American Society of Lubrication Engineers*.]

marked by an intermediate zone. In this intermediate zone a very good approximation to the full elasto-hydrodynamic solution is obtained when the solids are assumed to be rigid and the lubricant viscosity is allowed to vary with pressure. The pressures generated by increasing loads initially influence the lubricant viscosity and produce an enhanced load carrying capacity for a given minimum film thickness long before the effects of elastic deformation become significant. This observation is valid for steel cylinders lubricated by a mineral oil; a combination of material properties which leads to a value of G close to 5000. For very soft solids the reverse situation will apply and the more comprehensive diagram presented by Koets must be consulted.

The nature of a lubricated steel contact can readily be determined by computing the dimensionless speed (U) and load (W) parameters and locating the corresponding point in one of the three zones shown in Fig. 7.19. An interesting feature of Fig. 7.19 is that it shows that the Martin formula underestimates the film thickness in the "elastic" zone whilst the elasto-hydrodynamic formula *underestimates* the film thickness in the "rigid" zone. The problem in the past has been to select the appropriate formula for film thickness calculation. The definition of the intermediate zone and its representation in Fig. 7.19 helps to overcome this difficulty. The zones indicate the regions in which fluid property variations and/or the elastic distortion of the solids can be neglected.

A Note About Thermal Effects

The theoretical solutions presented so far have all been related to isothermal conditions, and it would thus appear that the range of application of the results is limited to contacts in pure rolling. However, a good deal of experimental information has now demonstrated that the film thickness formula (7.1) can give remarkably good predictions of the minimum film thickness in contacts in which some sliding occurs. The important point is that the viscosity of the lubricant in the immediate vicinity of the inlet to the contact must be employed in the calculation of film thickness.

Theoretical confirmation of the wide range of application of the isothermal formula has been presented by Cheng and Sternlicht (1964). In this paper Cheng and Sternlicht tackled the difficult mathematical problem presented by a mixed rolling and sliding contact.

By considering a uniform viscosity across the oil film a method was developed in which simultaneous solutions of the energy, elasticity and Reynolds equations could be obtained using a combination of "direct" and "inverse" iterations. It was found to be expedient to fix the location of the pressure spike and to seek the corresponding speed as the numerical procedure progressed.

The results presented by Cheng and Sternlicht are most interesting. One important feature which emerges from the calculations is the persistence of the sharp pressure peak in the presence of sliding. Indeed the results show that the height of the pressure peak may increase as the sliding velocity, and hence the temperature rise within the lubricant, increases.

Perhaps the most important conclusion reached by Cheng and Sternlicht is that the temperature has a moderate influence upon the minimum film thickness. Although the temperature rise in the contact zone can be considerable (Cheng and Sternlicht quote values of mean temperature rise in excess of 50°C), the temperature rise in the all important inlet zone is relatively small in all cases.

EXAMPLES. It will be useful at this stage to calculate the film thicknesses for the gears and roller bearing examined in Chapter 4 by rigid cylinder theory. The main problem for the designer is to estimate the bulk temperature of the solids, on which to base the value of η_0; or, for a given film thickness, to determine the necessary η_0.

1. The gears:

$$R = 20 \text{ mm}, \quad u = 5 \text{ m/s}, \quad w = 2\cdot5 \text{ MN/m}$$

$$\eta_0 = 0\cdot075 \text{ Pas}$$

For steel,

$$E' = 2 \cdot 3 \times 10^{11} \text{ Pa} = 3 \cdot 3 \times 10^7 \text{ lb/in}^2$$

For steel and mineral oil, $G \approx 5000$

$$W = \frac{w}{E'R} = 5 \cdot 4 \times 10^{-4}$$

(this corresponds to a maximum Hertzian pressure of about 2 GPa $= 130 \text{ ton/in}^2$)

$$U = \frac{\eta_0 u}{E'R} = 8 \cdot 15 \times 10^{-11}$$

$$\frac{h}{R} = 1 \cdot 6 \frac{G^{0 \cdot 6} U^{0 \cdot 7}}{W^{0 \cdot 13}} = 6 \cdot 1 \times 10^{-5}$$

Therefore $h = 1 \cdot 2$ μm. (48 μin.), compared with the rigid cylinder result $0 \cdot 015$ μm .

2. The roller bearing:

$$R = 6 \cdot 4 \text{ mm.,} \quad u = 10 \cdot 05 \text{ m./s,} \quad w = 0 \cdot 3 \text{ } MN/\text{m.}$$

$$\eta_0 = 0 \cdot 01 \text{ Pa s}$$

$$W = 2 \cdot 1 \times 10^{-4}$$

$$U = 7 \cdot 05 \times 10^{-11}$$

$$\frac{h}{R} = 6 \cdot 2 \times 10^{-5}$$

Therefore $h = 0 \cdot 4$ μm. (15 μin.), compared with the rigid cylinder result of $0 \cdot 01$ μm.

The combined effects of elasticity and viscosity variation have increased the theoretical film thickness under given conditions by nearly two orders of magnitude in these two practical cases. The film thicknesses predicted by the fuller theory are substantially greater than the roughnesses of the surface which are commonly prepared on standard engineering components. According to this theory then there is a healthy prospect of full hydrodynamic lubrication.

CHAPTER 8

EXPERIMENTAL BACKGROUND

NEARLY all experimental work on elasto-hydrodynamic lubrication has been carried out since 1950. However, long before this time, operating experience with gears and other highly loaded lubricated contacts had suggested that the solids might be separated by a fluid film under some conditions. Much of the evidence was indirect and inconclusive, but the persistence of machining marks and the lack of serious surface damage provided

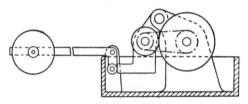

FIG. 8.1. Diagram of Merritt's disk machine.
[Reproduced by kind permission from the *Proceedings of the Institution of Mechanical Engineers*, Vol. 129, p. 127 (1935).]

the strongest case in support of hydrodynamic lubrication. In addition, the measured efficiency of gears suggested that the friction force generated in the tooth contact was more representative of fluid film conditions than of boundary friction or metallic contact.

A notable step forward was taken by Merritt (1935) when he designed and built a *disk machine* which simulated gear tooth contact conditions. In this machine, which is shown diagramatically in Fig. 8.1, two disks are pressed together with a known force and rotated at known speeds. The torque due to friction is measured by a dynamometer. The two disks are selected to represent any particular contact geometry and in Merritt's experiments one disk was made of bronze and the other of steel.

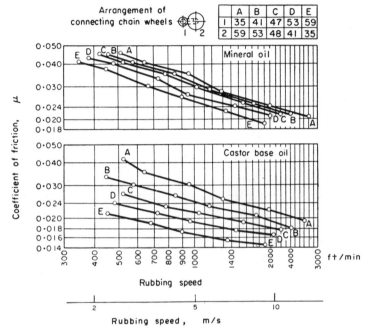

FIG. 8.2. Experimental results obtained from Merritt's disk machine.

[Reproduced by kind permission from the *Proceedings of the Institution of Mechanical Engineers*, Vol. 129, p. 127 (1935).]

The disk machine can, of course, be used to evaluate gear materials and lubricants, and until recently this has been its main role.

In the present context the feature of Merritt's work which is of particular interest is the measurement of coefficient of friction. The two shafts carrying the test disks were chain driven and various combinations of sliding and rolling velocities could be achieved. The experimental values of the friction coefficient obtained by Merritt are shown plotted against sliding speed in

Fig. 8.2. This work presented valuable data on the friction conditions in gears, and the disk machine is now a standard piece of equipment for the examination of highly loaded contacts.

Film Thickness

No direct attempt to record the existence of a fluid film in representative gear contacts was made by Merritt, and it was some 15–20 years later that this aspect of the subject started to attract attention. Lane and Hughes (1952) described an interesting study of oil film formation in gears by *electrical resistance* methods. The potential difference across insulated gears on a modified I.A.E. gear rig was recorded on a cathode ray oscilloscope whilst the gears were in motion. Although the results were necessarily qualitative in nature because of uncertainty about the electrical properties of lubricants under contact conditions, they clearly demonstrated the existence of effective lubricating films. The authors estimated that the resistance of an oil film 10^{-7} m thick between the gears would have a value in excess of $10^9\ \Omega$, and consequently resistances of the order of a few ohms must indicate some metallic contact or extremely thin films. Some of the records from this work are shown in Fig. 8.3, and the authors note that the resistance (and hence the film thickness) decreases with sliding speed and load.

Cameron (1954) noted that the electrical characteristics of an oil film depended upon the current. For currents less than about 0·5 A the oil film resistance was found to depend upon the applied voltage; the oil behaving almost like an ohmic resistance. At higher currents the voltage drop across the film (i.e. the *discharge voltage*) was effectively constant. The possibility of relating resistance measurements to oil film thickness was discussed in detail by Lewicki (1955). For various reasons Lewicki decided that the resistance method could not lead to a satisfactory measurement of film thickness. His main objection was based on the effect of transients; the influence of surface asperities and stray particles of suspended matter in the lubricant clearly being of considerable importance.

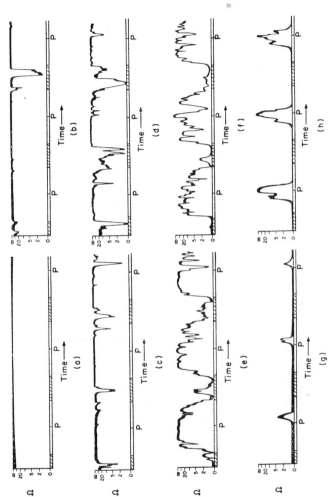

Fig. 8.3. Oscillograph traces showing the variation of oil-film resistance with meshing position when using a mineral oil of viscosity 0·13 Pas at the operating temperature of 333K (60°C). Pinion speed: 2500 rev/min. (a) 44·5N (10 lbf) beginning of run. (b) 89N (20 lbf) beginning of run. (c) 89N (20 lbf) end of run. (d) 133N (30 lbf) beginning of run. (e) 178N (40 lbf) beginning of run. (f) 222N (50 lbf) before scuffing. (g) 222N (50 lbf) after scuffing. (h) 178N (40 lbf) scuffed gear.

[Reproduced from the *British Journal of Applied Physics*, Vol. 3, p. 315 (1952) by kind permission of the Institute of Physics and The Physical Society.]

Lewicki constructed a disk machine in which two hard brass cylinders were loaded together and lubricated by a machine oil containing a trace of paraffin. The film thickness was deduced from measurements of the *capacitance* of the disk–oil film–disk system using a low voltage radio-frequency signal. Although the dielectric constant of the lubricant was assumed to be constant (i.e. independent of pressure, temperature and shear rate), and the assumed shape of the gap between the deformed cylinders is now known to be in error, some of Lewicki's findings are of considerable interest. Furthermore, this work heralded the arrival of film capacitance measurements as a technique for film thickness determination. One of the significant results obtained by Lewicki was that the oil film thickness was of the order of 10^{-6} m; – a value later found to be representative of such contacts by Crook. The importance of the bulk disk temperature in film thickness determination was also noted.

Crook (1958) discussed the weakness of the voltage discharge method in a paper in which he presented the first reliable measurements of film thickness. Crook neatly overcame the problems associated with the incertainty about electrical characteristics of lubricants under contact conditions by measuring the *volume rate of flow* through the conjunction of the disks. The volume rate of flow, which was measured on the unloaded side of a disk, was obtained by recording the capacitance between a very lightly loaded pad and the disk. The pad floated on the thin layer of oil adhering to the disk surface, and since the lubricant was only subjected to small pressures the relationship between capacitance and film thickness could be established. The relationship was in fact determined in two ways. The extent of the continuous oil film and the disposition of the lubricant in the cavitated region was observed through a glass pad, and with the geometry specified the capacitance could be related to the film thickness. Secondly, the pad–oil film–disk capacitance was related to the disk–oil film–disk capacitance under lightly loaded conditions, and this again enabled the pad capacitance to be related to film thickness. The latter calibration was thought to be the more reliable and it was employed by Crook in his interpretation of the results. This work is discussed in detail in Chapter 9, and we will now return to a consideration of other experimental work.

In an attempt to develop the technique of film thickness determination from *electrical resistance* measurements, El-Sisi and Shawki (1960 a, b) found that the treatment of oils with some *additives* could enhance the independence of oil film resistance from temperature and electrical history. The current flow due to a constant a.c. potential of 0·5 V was recorded on a disk machine and the measurements related to film thickness by a static calibration. Even at the low loads employed in the tests the experimental film thickness in pure rolling was almost an order of magnitude greater than the theoretical predictions. Since the theoretical solutions neglect side-leakage, the minimum film thickness determined experimentally at low loads should be smaller than the theoretical prediction, and hence the electrical resistance method is still unsatisfactory.

Brix (1947) and Cameron (1954) had noted that the *discharge voltage* varied with the oil film thickness and this observation formed the basis of a method of measuring film thickness which was applied to gears by MacConochie and Cameron (1960). Although the calibration constant relating discharge voltage to film thickness was measured several times during the investigation and found to be constant at about 0·157 V per millionth of a metre, it was found to be considerably affected by dirt particles. This difficulty, and perhaps the surface irregularities on the gears, may account for the considerable scatter exhibited by the results. The results did, however, demonstrate the existence of an oil film of considerable thickness on the pitch line and the severity of the contact conditions at the tips of the teeth.

It is clear that the determination of film thickness by electrical capacitance measurements is the only satisfactory technique which has emerged so far. There is, however, another method which, for effective film thicknesses a few times greater than the height of the surface asperities, appears to be equally reliable. The method is based on a direct *X-ray transmission technique* and it was pioneered by Sibley, Bell, Orcutt and Allen (1960). A beam of X-rays of width 762 μm (0·03 in.) is directed at the contact between two lubricated rollers of a disk machine, and the amount of the X-ray beam that passes through the gap is measured by a radiation counter and thus related to film thickness. The arrangement of the apparatus is shown in Fig. 8.4. A molybdenum X-ray source is employed since the radiation

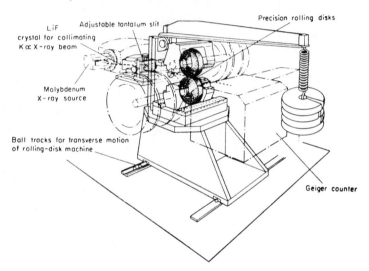

FIG. 8.4. Sketch of precision rolling—disk machine and X-ray system.

[Reproduced from *WADD Technical Report* 60–189 (1960) by Sibley, L. B., Bell, J. C., Orcutt, F. K., and Allen, C. M. (U.S.A.F. Contract AF 33(616)–5109) by kind permission of the Materials Laboratory, Aeronautical Systems Division, Wright-Patterson Air Force Base, Ohio and Battelle Memorial Institute, Ohio.]

penetrates lubricants quite readily and yet it will not penetrate bearing steels to any appreciable extent.

The disks, which were made integral with the shafts, were made from hardened bearing steel and each had a diameter of 0·058 m (2·28 in.). Each disk had a slight transverse curvature of 0·91 m (36 in.) radius to simulate the contact conditions in a typical ball bearing and the surfaces were lapped and polished to less than 0·0762 μm (3 μin.) r.m.s. surface finish. Three white mineral oils, a stable diester and a silicone lubricant were employed and film thicknesses ranging from 0·1 to 1·32 μm (4 to 52 μin.) were recorded. The estimated accuracy was 0·05 μm (2 μin.) over the following range of experimental conditions.

Rolling speed 8·6–26·4 m/s (1700–5200 ft/min)
Roller load 89–3648N (20–820 lbf)
Maximum Hertz stress 0·34–1·24 GPa (50,000 to 180,000 lbf/m^{-2})
Roller temperature 323K to 347K (122°F to 165°F)

The separation between the disk surfaces as measured by the X-ray transmission technique is compared with the true separation between the disks in Fig. 8.5. The effect of load on the transverse profiles of the contact is shown in Fig. 8.6, where the effect of elastic distortion is clearly seen. Similarly, the beneficial effect of rolling speed upon film thickness is evident from the film shapes shown in Fig. 8.7.

A great number of film thickness measurements were obtained by the X-ray transmission technique. The results obtained at two loads have been plotted against a dimensionless group described by Sibley *et al.* as the contact-lubrication flow number and compared with Grubin's formula as shown in Figs. 8.8 and 8.9. It will be noted that the experimental results are all slightly lower than Grubin's predicted film thickness but that the slopes of the theoretical and experimental results are remarkably similar. This observation ceases to hold for film thicknesses less than about 0·25 μm (10^{-5} in.) and this deviation is probably caused by surface irregularities; the sum of the surface irregularities being of order 0·25 μm (10^{-5} in.).

These interesting experiments based on the X-ray transmission technique demonstrate many of the essential characteristics of highly loaded lubricated contacts. The film thickness measurements stand with Crook's results to form the most reliable experimental information currently available. The relationship between experimental results and predictions based upon the the-

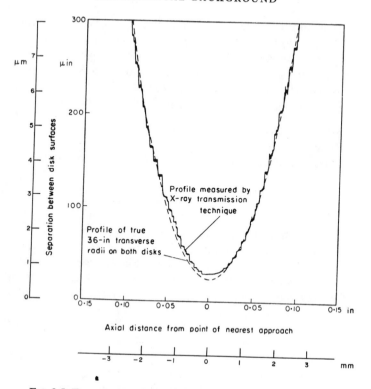

FIG. 8.5. Transverse profile of separation between rollers under no load.

[Reproduced from *WADD Technical Report* 60–189 (1960) by Sibley, L. B., Bell, J. C., Orcutt, F. K., and Allen, C. M. (U.S.A.F. Contract AF33(616)–5109) by kind permission of the Materials Laboratory, Aeronautical Systems Division, Wright-Patterson Air Force Base, Ohio and Battelle Memorial Institute, Ohio.]

oretical analysis of previous chapters will be discussed later.

A remarkable demonstration of the persistence of hydro-dynamic films under conditions of nominal point contact has been given by Archard and Kirk (1961). In an apparatus in which two rotating steel cylinders having their axes mutually at right angles were loaded together it was found that oil film thicknesses ranging from 0·05 to 2·54 μm (2 to 100 μin.) could be detected. Archard and Kirk, whose results are discussed in Chapter 9,

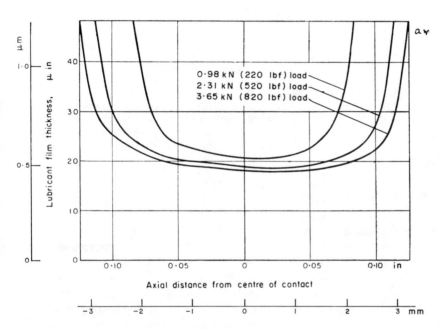

FIG. 8.6. Effect of load on film shape between rollers 15×10^{-6} m²/s White mineral oil (326 K (128°F) roller temperature), 13·2 m/s (2600 ft/min) rolling speed. Smooth curves have been drawn through profile traces.

[Reproduced from *WADD Technical Report* 60–189 (1960) by Sibley, L.B., Bell, J.C., Orcutt, F.K., and Allen, C.M.(U.S.A.F. Contract AF 33(616)–5109) by kind permission of the Materials Laboratory, Aeronautical Systems Division, Wright-Patterson Air Force Base, Ohio and Battelle Memorial Institute, Ohio.]

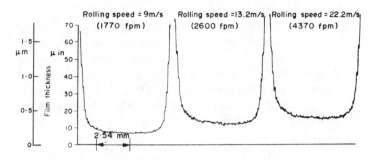

FIG. 8.7. Effect of rolling speed on film shape between rollers.
Load = 3·6 kN (820 lbf) disk temperature 339 K (150°F) (10·8 ×
10⁻⁶m²/s white mineral oil).

[Reproduced from *WADD Technical Report* 60–189 (1960) by
Sibley, L.B., Bell, J.C., Orcutt, F.K., and Allen, C.M. (U.S.A.F.
Contract AF 33(616)–5109) by kind permission of the Materials
Laboratory, Aeronautical Systems Division, Wright-Patterson
Air Force Base, Ohio and Battelle Memorial Institute, Ohio.]

concluded that hydrodynamic lubrication occurred much more
frequently and boundary lubrication much less frequently than
is usually supposed.

The experiments described above which yielded reliable measurements of film thickness employed disks whose surfaces were
as fine as engineering processes can produce; the height of the
surface irregularities being only a fraction of a micro-metre (a few
micro-inches). Very few real engineering components can match
this surface quality (the rolling elements in rolling bearings being
the only common ones). Gear teeth have surfaces much worse
than those of the best disks, and suffer from macroscopic geometrical imperfections in addition. Gears and rolling bearings
frequently operate in conditions such that the calculated film
thickness is about the same as the known height of the surface
irregularities. The quest for the nature of the mechanism of such
contacts presents the most important outstanding problem in the
subject. Dawson's work (1961, 1962) on the fatigue life of the
components in such situations is well known. Recently Tallian

et al. (1964) have published the results of an investigation into the "rough contact" situation in a rolling four-ball machine. They detected contact of the surface asperities by fine measurement of wear rates and, separately, by measurements of electrical conductivity of the oil film, incorporating a count of asperity contacts. They correlated the extent of contact with that which would be expected from a statistical analysis of the measured surface geometry, and as a result deduced values of film thickness which were in close agreement with those predicted by the theoretical

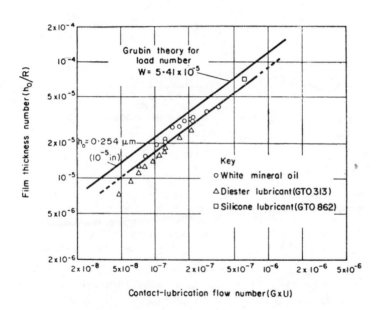

FIG. 8.8. Plot of dimensionless parameters for film thickness measurements at 0·98 kN (220 lbf) load. Load number W for 0·98 kN (220 lbf) load = $5·41 \times 10^{-5}$.

[Reproduced from *WADD Technical Report* 60–189 (1960) by Sibley, L.B., Bell, J.C., Orcutt, F.K., and Allen, C.M. (U.S.A.F. Contract AF 33(616)–5109) by kind permission of the Materials Laboratory, Aeronautical Systems Division, Wright-Patterson Air Force Base, Ohio and Battelle Memorial Institute, Ohio.]

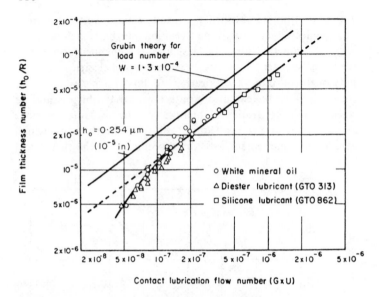

Fig. 8.9. Plot of dimensionless parameters for film thickness measurements at 3·65 kN (820 lbf) load. Load number W for 3·65 kN (820 lbf) load $= 1·3 \times 10^{-4}$.

[Reproduced from *WADD Technical Report* 60–189 (1960) by Sibley, L.B., Bell, J.C., Orcutt, F.K., and Allen, C.M. (U.S.A.F. Contract AF 33(616)–5109) by kind permission of the Materials Laboratory, Aeronautical Systems Division, Wright-Patterson Air Force Base, Ohio and Battelle Memorial Institute, Ohio.]

expression of Archard and Kirk (1961). Christensen (1964a) describes a similar approach in experiments on a two-disk machine with nominal line contact.

Oil Film Shape

The two notable features of elasto-hydrodynamic film shapes, namely the near-parallel film followed by a restriction or step near the outlet end of the contact, have been recorded experi-

mentally. Kodnir (1960) discussed the reasons for the existence
of a step and he carried out experiments to measure the film
shape in a non-metallic bearing. An insulated electrode was in-
serted in a rotating shaft and the surface of the non-metallic
(bakelite) bearing was covered with tin foil 10 μm thick. The
capacitance across the oil film was recorded on an oscilloscope
during rotation. A typical trace shows a gap of almost constant
film thickness over a substantial part of the pressure zone with a
restriction presenting the minimum film thickness near outlet.

When water is employed as a lubricant the step is much
reduced and the film profile adopts a nearly linear form.

Kodnir ascribed this result to the fact that the viscosity of
water is essentially independent of pressure, and he adopts this
argument to explain why a non-metallic bearing lubricated by
water frequently operates more successfully than one lubricated
by oil. Kodnir points out that Poisson's ratio for many non-
metallic bearing materials is close to 0·5 and the generation of
high pressures (encouraged by the pressure–viscosity effect in
oils) in the contact zone leads to a squashing of the bearing
material in the high pressure region and an expansion on either
side. This leads to the formation of two regions of reduced film
thickness, one at inlet and one at outlet, and Kodnir provides
experimental confirmation of this prediction. The effect is far
greater with oil than with water and the restriction at inlet hinders
the flow of oil into the contact zone.

A similar experimental technique has been employed by Crook
(1961 c) on a four-disk machine employing a glass central disk.
In this case a thin chromium electrode was evaporated onto the
glass disk. As the electrode passed through the conjunction of
the disks the change in capacitance was converted into a voltage
and interpreted in terms of film thickness. The signal was por-
trayed on an oscilloscope and the essential features of the film
shape were at once apparent. These experiments together with
the appropriate theory are fully described in Chapter 9.

Coefficient of Friction

Although film thickness measurement has quite rightly formed the central feature of most experimental investigations in elasto-hydrodynamic lubrication, friction coefficients and pressure distributions have also received some attention in recent years.

The magnitude of the coefficient of friction in a highly loaded disk machine was examined by Misharin (1958) at high rolling and sliding speeds. Two fine ground steel disks of diameters 60 mm and 90 mm respectively were tested at contact stresses up to 0.88GPa, rolling velocities $(u_1 + u_2)$ up to 23 m/s and sliding velocities $(u_2 - u_1)$ up to 12 m/s; the friction torque being determined from dynamometer readings. The bulk temperature of the smaller disk, as recorded by a thermocouple, was controlled by heating or cooling the lubricant and adjusting its flow rate.

Misharin presented an approximate formula for the calculation of friction coefficient based upon a vast number of experimental results. The formula can be written as,

$$\mu = \frac{0.325 \times 10^6}{(v(u_1 + u_2)(u_2 - u_1))^{1/4}}$$

where v = kinematic viscosity (m²/s)

u_1, u_2 = surface velocities (m/s).

This formula does not give realistic results at very high or very low values of the rolling or sliding speeds. (It will be noted that $\mu \to \infty$ as the condition of pure rolling is approached.) Consequently Misharin suggests that the formula should be applied to steel contacts lubricated by mineral oils under the following conditions.

σ (contact stress) > 0.245GPa   (35,560 lbf/in²)

$$\left(\frac{u_2 - u_1}{u_1 + u_2} \right) = 0 \cdot 2 \to 0 \cdot 65$$

FIG. 8.10. Arrangement of skewed disk.

[Reproduced by kind permission of the Division of Mechanical
Engineering, National Research Council of Canada.]

the values of μ to be within the range,

$$0\!\cdot\!08 \geqq \mu \geqq 0\!\cdot\!02$$

If the calculated coefficient is outside this range the appropriate limiting value (0·08 or 0·02) should be used.

El-Sisi and Shawki (1958) measured friction torques on the disk machine employed in the film thickness investigation described earlier. A dynamometer was employed and an allowance was made for extraneous bearing torques. This approach may jeopardize the measurement of small torques, such as occur in pure rolling, but the recorded friction coefficients at significant slip velocities are remarkably consistent with other results (see for example, Misharin, Smith, F.W., and Crook).

Smith (1959) employed a *skewed disk machine* to investigate friction forces in highly loaded contacts. The driving disk was cylindrical and the driven disk spherical; the radius of each disk being 25·4 mm (one inch). The skewing of the rollers caused an axial force to act on the driven roller and this force was recorded by a strain gauge dynamometer. The axial force was interpreted as the component of force required to shear the contact zone with a sliding velocity $U \sin \alpha$. This transverse sliding velocity is superimposed upon the rolling velocity U, and α is the skew angle between the disk axes.

The skewed disk machine was later developed into the form shown in Figs. 8.10 and 8.11. Smith (1962) presented an interesting set of results obtained from the machine which showed the variation of friction coefficient with sliding speed at different rolling speeds, contact stresses and temperatures. The temperature was recorded in the air space near to the contact. A typical graph is shown in Fig. 8.12. It can be seen that the friction coefficient increases to a maximum and then decreases as the sliding speed is increased. If the lubricant behaved like a Newtonian fluid under isothermal conditions throughout the experiment the relationship between friction coefficient and sliding speed would be linear. Smith (1962) points out that the initial relationship is almost linear and he attributes the subsequent deviation to thermal and non-Newtonian effects.

It is interesting to note that Crook (1963 a) also found a maximum on his friction traction–sliding speed graphs. Crook's measurement of friction represents the fourth work on this aspect of the subject which will be referred to. By designing an ingenious *four-disk machine* in which the driven disk is entirely supported by the other three, Crook was able to measure the very small friction torques encountered at low slip velocities with high accuracy. This made possible the estimation of rolling friction torques and the interesting result, predicted in Chapter 7, that the surface traction under these conditions is proportional to film thickness was confirmed.

Before leaving the question of friction forces in highly loaded contacts it is instructive to compare the essential features of the results obtained from the experiments described above. The main influences on coefficient of friction which need to be

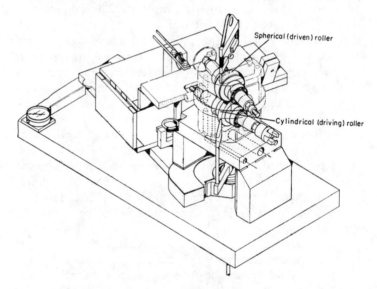

Spherical (driven) roller

Cylindrical (driving) roller

Fig. 8.11. Details of Smith's "skewed" rolling contact disk machine.

[Reproduced by kind permission of the Division of Mechanical Engineering, National Research Council of Canada.]

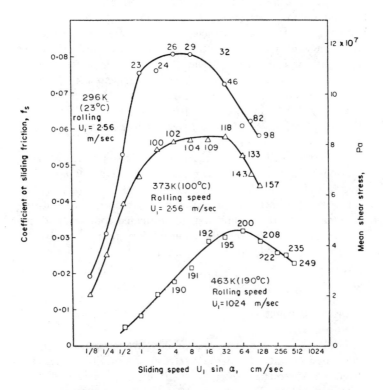

Fig. 8.12. Coefficient of friction f_s for steel rollers as function of sliding speed $U_1 \sin \alpha$. Mean normal stress σ_m, 1·791 GPa (259,700 lb/in²).

[Reproduced from *ASLE Transactions* Vol. 5, p. 142 (1962) by kind permission of the American Society of Lubrication Engineers.]

examined are rolling velocity, sliding velocity, temperature and load. Table 8.1 lists the effects of these variables as determined by different investigators together with a summary of the approximate range of friction coefficients encountered. Two features of the table worthy of note are the general consistency in the range of values of friction coefficient encountered in these four independent experiments and the overall agreement as to the effect of the principal variables. One exception to this generalization is the effect of temperature on friction forces found by Smith. The temperatures were unfortunately recorded in different places by the four experimenters.

Smith recorded the temperature in the air space near the contact point, El-Sisi and Shawki measured the oil inlet temperature and Misharin and Crook considered the disk temperatures. The latter workers both drew attention to the important role of surface temperatures in highly loaded lubricated contacts, and this observation may explain the contradictory result obtained by Smith when he related his measurements to the local air temperature.

Pressure Distribution

The very small dimensions of effective pressure zones in lubricated contacts of low geometrical conformity renders the direct measurement of pressure distribution extremely difficult. We have seen in Chapter 7 that the oil film pressures in elastic contacts have distinctive shapes, and we will end our historical survey of elasto-hydrodynamic experiments by considering some recent investigations of pressure profiles.

In a model experiment in elasto-hydrodynamic lubrication Higginson (1962) recorded the oil film pressures in a contact formed between a 0·27 m (10½ in.) dia. *bronze drum* and a *block of rubber*. Owing to the low elastic modulus of rubber 1·72 MPa (250 lb/in²) very low pressures were encountered and the effect of pressure on viscosity was therefore lost. However, the gradual transition from a pressure distribution representative of rigid

TABLE 8.1

Name	Range of μ encountered	Effect on coefficient of friction (μ) of an *increase* in:			
		rolling velocity $(u_1 + u_2)$	sliding velocity $(u_2 - u_1)$	temperature	load
Misharin, J.A. (1958)	0·025 → 0·07	μ falls	μ falls	μ rises	μ almost independent of load
El-Sisi, S.I. and Shawki, G.S.A. (1960b)	0 → 0·047	μ falls	μ rises to a maximum when one disc becomes stationary and then falls to an almost constant value for contra-rotation	μ rises	μ increases very slightly
Smith, F.W. (1962)	0 → 0·08	μ falls	μ increases at first, often reaches a maximum and then falls	μ falls	μ increases
Crook, A.W. (1963a)	0·02 → 0·05	μ falls	μ increases at first, reaches a maximum and then falls	μ rises	μ increases

solids to a near Hertzian pressure curve at higher loads is clearly seen in Fig. 8.13. The small temperatures encountered in the contact enabled Higginson to examine the pressure distributions along the lines of the inverse hydrodynamic analysis discussed in Chapter 6. The calculated film thickness is plotted against load and compared with the predictions of elementary rigid cylinder theory in Fig. 8.14. The beneficial effect of elastic distortion on film thickness is plain to see.

Dowson and Longfield (1963 b) have described an experimental investigation of the pressure distribution in a lubricated sliding

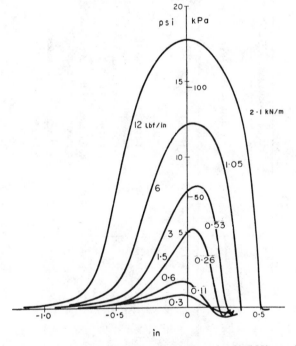

FIG. 8.13. Pressure distributions for various loads (kN/m and lbf/in.). Rubber block experiment.

[Reproduced from the *International Journal of Mechanical Science*, Vol. 4, pp. 205–10 (1962) by kind permission of Pergamon Press.]

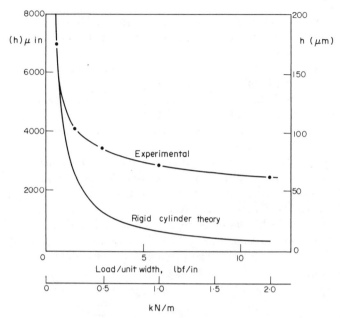

FIG. 8.14. Variation of film thickness with load. Rubber block experiment.

[Reproduced from the *International Journal of Mechanical Science* Vol. 4, pp. 205–10 (1962) by kind permission of Pergamon Press.]

contact formed between two bronze surfaces. A substantial Hertzian contact width was achieved by the use of surfaces having a large effective radius of curvature. This requirement was satisfied by running a 0·3 m (12 in.) dia. *bronze disk* on a *concave bronze surface* as shown in Fig. 8.15. Loads up to almost 0·88 MN/m (5000 lb/in.) were applied hydraulically and, in addition to the oil film pressures, temperatures within the stationary solid were recorded. The associated film shapes were calculated by an inverse hydrodynamic calculation based upon the temperatures of the stationary metal surface and the oil film pressures.

The oil film pressure distributions corresponding to various loads are shown in Fig. 8.16. In addition, contours of temperatures within the stationary solid are shown together with the estimated film shapes. The notable features of these results are the steepening of the outlet pressure curve with increasing load, the emergence of a characteristic elasto-hydrodynamic film shape and the occurrence of a maximum stationary surface temperature before the end of the pressure zone.

In some further experiments on the same apparatus Dowson and Longfield (1964) examined the variation of pressure and temperature within the contact zone in both the axial and circumferential direction.

In these experiments a steel disk of diameter 0·302 m (11·9 in.) and track width 0·01 m (0·4 in.) was used and the stationary shoe of concave radius 0·164 m (6·473 in.) was made of phosphor bronze. Two cases were investigated; a low load of approximately 0·525 MN/m (3000 lb/in.) which produced only a small elastic deformation, and a high load of approximately 1·36 MN/m (7750 lb/in.) which produced an elasto-hydrodynamic regime.

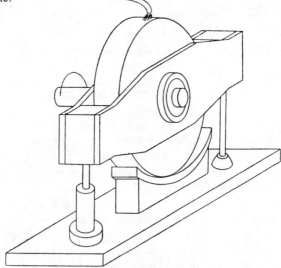

FIG. 8.15. Diagramatic arrangement of high conformity disk machine.
[Reproduced by kind permission from the *Proceedings of the Institution of Mechanical Engineers Lubrication and Wear Convention* (1963)].

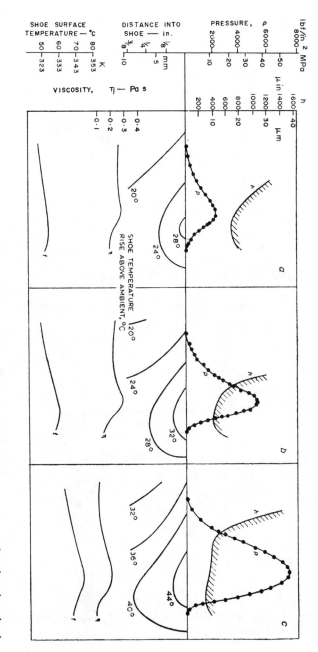

FIG. 8.16. Pressure, temperature, viscosity and film thickness profiles for a constant speed and various loads. (a) Load 0·077 MN/m (440 lb/in.) (b) Load 0·231 MN/m (1320 lb/in.) (c) Load 0·385 MN/m (2200 lb/in.)

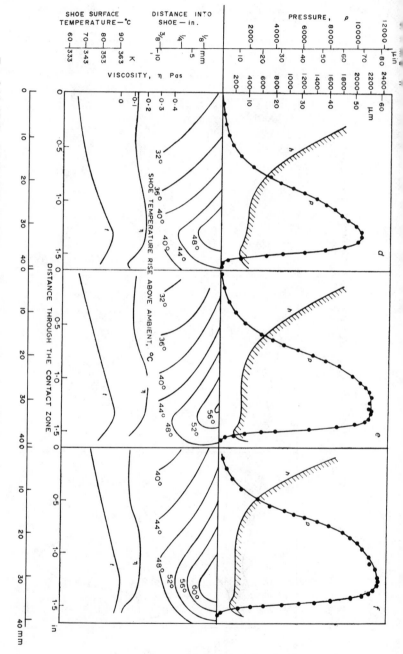

FIG. 8.16. (d) Load 0·54 MN/m (3080 lb/in.) (e) Load 0·69 MN/m (3960 lb/in.) (f) Load 0·85 MN/m (4840 lb/in.) [Reproduced by kind permission from the *Proceedings of the Institution of Mechanical Engineers Lubrication and Wear Convention* (1963)].

The variation of pressure and temperature over the contact zone for both cases is shown in Figs. 8.17 and 8.18. A feature of the high-load case shown in Fig. 8.17 is the very large axial pressure gradients which occur near the edge of the contact. The pressure falls relatively slowly in the axial direction from about 96·5 MPa (14000 lb/in²) near the circumferential axis of symmetry to 55·2 MPa (8000 lb/in²) very near to the edge of the contact. This flat topped pressure variation in the axial direction supports the assumption that side leakage is of little importance in elasto-hydrodynamic contacts.

Figure 8.18 shows that the axial decay of temperature is small compared with the circumferential variation for both loads.

The shape of the oil film was deduced from the pressure and temperature measurements by means of the inverse hydro-

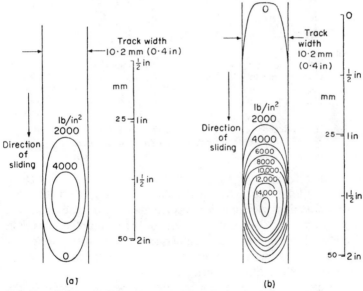

FIG. 8.17. Pressure contours in contact zone. (a) Load 0·53 MN/m (3000 lb/in.) (b) Load 1·36 MN/m (7750 lb/in.).

[Reproduced by kind permission from the *Proceedings of the Institution of Mechanical Engineers Third Annual Meeting of the Lubrication and Wear Group*, Cardiff 1964].

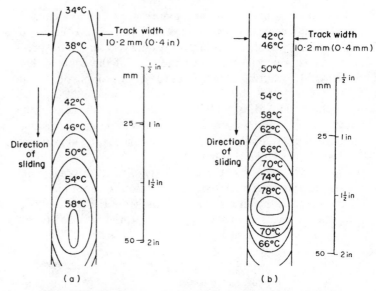

Fig. 8.18. Temperature contours in contact zone. (a) Load 0·53 MN/m (3000 lb/in.); mean disk-surface temperature 317 K (44°C); ambient temperature 295 K (22°C.) (b) Load 1·36 MN/m (7750 lb/in.); mean disk-surface temperature 52°C; ambient temperature 293 K (20°C).

[Reproduced by kind permission from the *Proceedings of the Institution of Mechanical Engineers Third Annual Meeting of the Lubrication and Wear Group,* Cardiff 1964]

dynamic calculation. By making one or two assumptions Dowson and Longfield were able to calculate the approximate variation of temperature and viscosity across the film. The results are shown in Figs. 8.19 and 8.20. One of the assumptions made in the analysis was that the temperature of the disk surface remained constant; an assumption that appears to be justified for the oil film conditions considered.

It can be seen that the maximum temperature occurs in the lower part of the oil film near to the stationary surface. The considerable temperature variation across the film leads to quite a spectacular viscosity variation as shown in Fig. 8.20. The effect of pressure upon viscosity is almost negated by the temperature

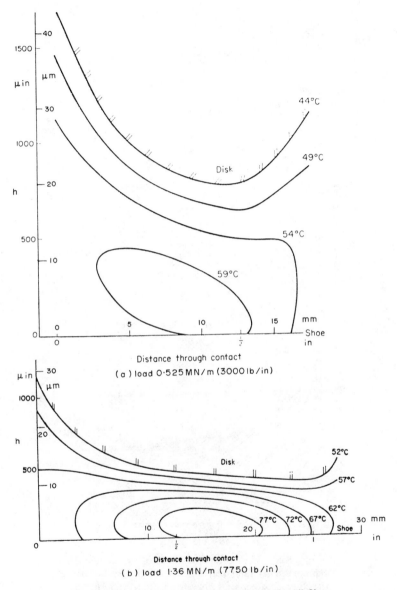

Fig. 8.19. Temperature distribution across the oil film.
[Reproduced by kind permission from the *Proceedings of the Institution of Mechanical Engineers Third Annual Meeting of the Lubrication and Wear Group*, Cardiff 1964]

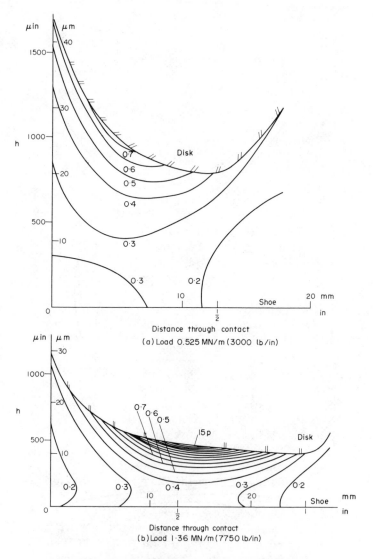

FIG. 8.20. Viscosity distribution across the oil film (Pas).
[Reproduced by kind permission from the *Proceedings of the
Institution of Mechanical Engineers Third Annual Meeting of the
Lubrication and Wear Group*, Cardiff 1964]

rise on the stationary surface, but no similar compensation is available on the moving surface.

Although the two experiments described above are related to contact conditions somewhat remote from engineering practice, they do demonstrate many of the essential features predicted in earlier chapters for elasto-hydrodynamic contacts. It should be noted that for these conditions elasto-hydrodynamic theory does not predict a pressure curve exhibiting the secondary pressure peak discussed in Chapter 7.

Niemann and Gartner (1964) have described experimental measurements of the circumferential and axial pressure distributions in a very small effective contact between small steel cylinders (radii 7·9–40 mm (0·31–1·58in.)) and the flat face of a rotating steel disk. A very small pressure tapping hole was produced by inserting a tight-fitting cylindrical plug, having a flat machined along its length, into a cylindrical hole.

The circular segment which formed the hole was a few hundredths of an inch wide in the axial direction and a few thousandths of an inch wide in the direction of sliding.

The pressure curves presented by Niemann and Gartner showed that side leakage was negligible and that the percentage of the load supported hydrodynamically decreased as the load increased. A singular distribution based upon five readings prompted the authors to suggest that the pressure spike predicted by elasto-hydrodynamic theory for a Newtonian fluid had been found, but a more exhaustive investigation will be needed.

Kannel, Bell and Allen (1964) have developed a pressure sensing system in which a thin film of manganin is deposited on an insulating disk. The method looks promising and measured pressure distributions for relatively light loads closely resemble the form of solution predicted by Martin for rigid cylinders. There was no evidence of the pressure spike predicted by elasto-hydrodynamic theory for a Newtonian fluid.

Finally, the history of elasto-hydrodynamic experiments described briefly in this chapter is summarized in Table 8.2. The list is by no means comprehensive, but the salient landmarks in the experimental development of the subject are exhibited.

TABLE 8.2. SUMMARY OF ELASTO-HYDRODYNAMIC EXPERIMENTS

Name	Date	Apparatus	Materials	Lubricant	Nominal contact conditions	Film thickness	Measurements	
							Friction torque	Pressure distribution
Merritt, H.E.	1935	Disk M/C	Steel–bronze	Mineral oil Caster oil	Line	—	✓	—
Lane, T.B. and Hughes, J.R.	1952	Disk M/C	Steel–steel	Mineral oil	Line	(Films detected by electrical resistance	—	—
Cameron, A.	1954	Disk M/C	Nickel steel	Mineral oil	Line	(Films detected by resistance current 1 amp.)	—	—
Lewicki, W.	1955	Disk M/C	Hard brass	Mineral oil	Line	(Electrical resistance. Film capacitance)	—	—
Crook, A.W.	1958 1961	Disk M/C	Hardened carbon steel	Mineral oil	Line	(Disk and pad capacitance)	—	—
Misharin, J.A.	1958	Disk M/C	Various steels	Mineral oil	Line	—	✓	—
El-Sisi, S.I. and Shawki, G.S.A.	1960 a,b	Disk M/C	Case hardened mild steel	Mineral oil and (additive)	Line	(Electrical conductivity)	✓	—
MacConochie, I.O. and Cameron, A.	1960	Back to back gear testing machine	EN34 and EN32 case hardened steel	Mineral oil	Line	(Voltage discharge)	—	—

TABLE 8.2 (continued)

Name	Date	Apparatus	Materials	Lubricant	Nominal contact conditions	Measurements		
						Film thickness	Friction torque	Pressure distribution
Smith, F.W.	1959 ↓ 1962	Skewed disk M/C	Steel	Mineral oil	Point	—	✓	—
Sibley, Bell, Orcutt and Allen	1960	Disk M/C	Hardened bearing steel	White mineral oil, diester and silicone	Point	(X-ray transmission)	—	—
Kodnir, D.S.	1960	Partial journal bearing	Steel shaft-textolite and polyamide bearing	Mineral oil water	Line	(Capacitance)	✓	—
Archard, J.F. and Kirk, M.T.	1961	Crossed cylinders machine	Steel	Mineral oil	Point	(Capacitance)	—	—
Higginson, G.R.	1962	Stationary block loaded against rotating drum	Rubber–bronze	Mineral oil	Line	—	—	Bronze–rubber
Kirk, M.T.	1962	Crossed cylinders machine	Perspex	Mineral oil	Point	(Optical interference)	✓	—
Crook, A.W.	1961	Four-disk machine	Steel-glass	Mineral oil	Line	(Oil film shape by electrical capacitance)	—	—
	1963	Four-disk machine	Steel-steel	Mineral oil	Line	(Capacitance)	—	—

Table 8.2 (continued)

Name	Date	Apparatus	Materials	Lubricant	Nominal contact conditions	Measurements		
						Film thickness	Friction torque	Pressure distribution
Dowson, D. and Longfield, M.D.	1963	Rotating disk loaded against stationary concave shoe	Bronze-bronze	Mineral oil	Line	—	—	Bronze-bronze
	1964	Rotating disk loaded against stationary concave shoe	Steel disk Bronze shoe	Mineral oil	Line	—	—	Steel-bronze (measurements made in circumferential and axial directions)
Archard, J.F. and Kirk, M.T.	1963	Crossed cylinders machine	Steel, brass, perspex, glass graphite	Mineral oil	Point	(Electrical capacitance and optical interference)	✓	—
Galvin, G.D. Naylor, H. and Wilson, A.R.	1964	Disk M/C	Steel-steel	Mineral oil Caster oil	Line	(Capacitance)	—	—
Niemann, G. and Gartner, F.	1964	Stationary rollers loaded against the face of a rotating disk	Steel-steel	Mineral oil	Line	—	—	✓
Kannel, J.W. Bell, J.C. and Allen, C.M.	1964	Disk M/C	Glass-steel	Mineral oil	Point-Disks with 0.91m (36") radius crown	—	—	(Manganin film)

CHAPTER 9

APPARATUS AND MEASUREMENTS
OF FILM THICKNESS
AND FILM SHAPE

Apparatus

The bulk of the experiments to be described were performed using two types of disk machine (Crook, 1958, 1963a). The first, a *two-disk machine* shown in Fig. 9.1, was based, in principle upon an earlier apparatus described by Merritt (1935) (see Fig. 8.1). The disk A ran in bearings in the machine frame (not shown) and was driven by a variable speed motor. The disk B ran in self-aligning bearings in the swinging arms C and D which hung from the axle E. The disk B was driven through a Cardan shaft either by gears from the shaft driving disk A or by a separate variable speed motor. Both disks had diameters of 3 in. (76·2 mm) and were 0·75 in. (19·1 mm) wide.

The disks were loaded together by equal tensions in the horizontal cables F and G. Vertical movement of the disk B was restrained by the spring beam H to which the axle E was rigidly fixed and the frictional force at the conjunction of the disks caused a deflection of the beam H which was measured by the dial gauge I. Calibration of the system was by dead weight loadings. There are a number of precautions essential to the successful operation of this method of friction measurement (Crook, 1963a). The arrangement gave measurements which were independent of friction in the bearings and thus had advantages over more conventional systems using torque dynamometers.

With the *four-disk machine*, shown in Fig. 9.2, it was possible

139

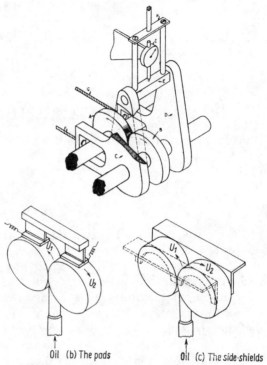

Oil (b) The pads   Oil (c) The side-shields

FIG. 9.1. (a) The two-disk machine. A + B. disks; C + D, swinging arms; E, axle; F + G, loading cables; H, spring beam. (b) The pads. (c) The side shields.

[Reproduced from *Philosophical Transactions* Vol. A255, p. 281 (1963) and Vol. A250, p. 387 (1958) by kind permission of the Royal Society.]

to measure the much smaller values of the friction obtained near to the rolling point. The two lower disks ran in bearings in the machine frame (not shown) while the disk C ran in self-aligning bearings in the pair of loading arms. The central disk D was supported entirely by the three outer disks and merely required an air thrust block E to provide axial location; in the context of the experiments which were performed the frictional drag imposed by this thrust block was imperceptible.

All four disks were nominally of 3 in. (76·2 mm) dia. The three outer disks were lapped to be equal in diameter to within 0·2 μm and were driven at equal speeds by the gear train F. In the friction experiments small external torques were applied to the inner disk by the band brake G which was designed to apply a pure torque. The machine was driven by a variable speed motor with a maximum speed of 3000 rev/min.

In order to attain pure rolling between the inner disk and any of the outer disks it would be necessary to apply a torque to both

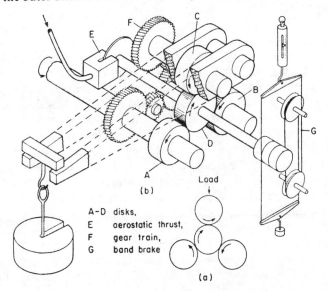

A–D disks,
E   aerostatic thrust,
F   gear train,
G   band brake

FIG. 9.2. The four-disk machine. (a) principle. (b) construction (diagrammatic).

[Reproduced from *Philosophical Transactions* Vol. A255, p. 281 (1963) by kind permission of the Royal Society.]

of their shafts to overcome the resistance due to rolling friction F_R. When the central disk is running freely without restraint it runs in the condition

$$F = F_R - F_S = 0$$

and a larger torque must be applied to the outer disks which now run in the condition

$$F = F_R + F_S$$

(see Crook, 1963a). Thus with no restraint on the inner disk it runs with a small amount of sliding relative to each of the outer disks such that F_S the frictional traction due to sliding is equal to the rolling friction F_R. When an external torque is applied to the inner disk this produces additional sliding between it and the outer disks.

In experiments with the disk machines the disks were in nominal line contact, a condition typical of roller bearings and most types of involute gears. In parallel experiments Archard and Kirk (1961) studied the lubrication of bodies in nominal point contact, a condition typical of ball bearings and some special forms of gears (e.g. crossed-axis helical gears). In this work a *crossed-cylinders machine* was used and the specimens consisted of rotating cylinders with their axes mutually at right angles. Although the theory of lubrication at point contacts is complicated by the influence of side-leakage these experiments showed that the effect of this factor is much less than might have been expected. Moreover since these measurements of film thickness closely parallel those obtained under conditions of line contact, it will be appropriate to discuss them in the present context.

All these machines were arranged with electrical insulation to permit the measurement of electrical capacitance between the specimens, for example, in the two-disk machine (Fig. 9.1) disk B was electrically insulated from the rest of the machine. It is important to ensure that the large stray capacitance formed by this insulation is independent of changes in temperature and therefore PTFE was used. Electrical connection to the shaft of B was made by a mercury contact of a type described by Kenyon (1954) whilst a similar contact gave a positive contact between disk A and earth; elasto-hydrodynamic lubrication makes the alternative earthing path through the roller bearings erratic.

The temperature of the specimens has a large influence upon

their lubrication and its accurate measurement is essential in any serious investigation. Two methods have been used and subsidiary tests have shown them to be in close agreement and reasonably free from error. In some experiments the surface temperature of the specimens was measured by thermocouples loaded against them with a load of a few grams. The junctions of the thermocouples were beaten into thin plates approximately 2 mm square. In other experiments the temperature of the specimens was measured by thermocouples embedded in them and disposed about 2 mm below the surfaces. Electrical connections to these thermocouples were made by means of mercury contacts.

In most of the experiments a mineral oil (turbine oil to Admiralty Specification OM 100) was used. Its viscosity ranges from 0·53 Pas at 10°C to 0·025 Pas at 60°C. Measurements of its viscosities at pressures up to 1000 bar have been made in a falling needle viscometer in a high pressure cell (Galvin, Naylor and Wilson, 1964). These results show that at low rates of shear the variation of viscosity with pressure follows, to a reasonable approximation, the exponential relation

$$\eta = \eta_0 \exp(\alpha p)$$

From the high pressure viscometer experiments the deduced values of α, the pressure coefficient, are $2 \cdot 2 \times 10^{-8}$ m^2/N at 60°C falling to $1 \cdot 7 \times 10^{-8}$ m^2/N at 100°C. In the experiments described below the specimen temperatures ranged between 15 and 50°C, and the appropriate values of α, estimated from results for a range of similar oils (A.S.M.E., 1953), are between 3·0 and 2·3 $\times 10^{-8}$ m^2/N.

Details of Electrical Measurements

Measurements of electrical capacitance were made at a frequency of 1000 Hz and a peak potential of 0·2 V using a Wien bridge (Hague, 1945). In balancing the bridge disturbances due to low resistance excursions were ignored. The causes of these disturbances have not been isolated but presumably they include contacts between surface asperities and the bridging of the gap between the surfaces by solid particles in the oil. In favourable conditions it is possible to measure the capacitance between loaded specimens with an accuracy better than ± 1 pF.

In interpreting these measurements the dielectric constant of the oil is clearly very important. This was measured at room temperature and atmospheric pressure at 1 kHz and was found to be 2·30. The dielectric constants of lubricating oils and their theoretical significance have been discussed by a number of authors (see, for example, Bondi, 1951). Only if the oil is polar (in the electrical sense) will the measured value at atmospheric pressure and room temperature require major correction when applied to the high pressures and temperatures which occur in the gap between heavily loaded specimens. For a non-polar oil it is reasonable to assume that the dielectric constant varies only on account of changes in density, i.e. the dielectric constant, ε, obeys the Clausius–Mosotti relationship

$$(\varepsilon - 1)/(\varepsilon + 2)\varrho = \text{constant}$$

where ϱ is the density. Measurements of ε and ϱ up to 250 °C satisfied this equation thus demonstrating that the oil was non-polar. Supporting evidence was also provided by measurements of the refractive index.

When a non-polar oil is used the major ambiguity in interpreting the inter-specimen capacitance concerns the shape of the gap. In his early experiments Crook (1958) used this method only at very light loads when it could be assumed that the surfaces were undistorted. At heavier loads Archard and Kirk (1961) showed that their measurements of inter-specimen capacitance at point contacts were consistent with the assumption that the surfaces had the Hertzian shape forecast by elasto-hydrodynamic theory; values of the minimum film thickness were then deduced on the basis of this assumption.

Measurement of Film Thickness Using Pads

Because of the possible ambiguities associated with the shape of the surfaces Crook (1958) devised a method which was independent of the distortion of the specimens. It was observed (Crook, 1957) that the oil passing between loaded disks leaves their conjunction forming films upon their surfaces. Stationary, lightly loaded, pads were arranged to ride upon these surface films (Fig. 9.1 b) and the capacitance between each pad and its disk was measured. From these capacitances the *rate of flow of oil* between the disks was deduced and, by a relationship of general validity, the film thickness at the pressure maximum was calculated.

The pads, shown in Fig. 9.1 b, were hardened steel plates 0·5 in. (12·7 mm) wide and 1·5 in. (38·1 mm) long, lapped both flat and smooth. A knife-edge arrangement held the pads in position and left them self-aligning. The load on each pad was less than 5N. The Perspex side shields shown in Fig. 9.1c excluded extraneous oil and ensured that only the oil passing between the disks reached the pads.

According to hydrodynamic theory the volume rate of oil flow Q between the disks is given by the expression

$$Q = \tfrac{1}{2}(u_1 + u_2)h_m \qquad (9.1)$$

Thus the volume rate of oil flow is proportional to h_m the film thickness at the pressure maximum; this is true even when the loads are sufficiently large to cause deformation of the disks or an increase in the viscosity of the oil. (A small correction may be needed later to allow for compressibility of the oil.) This volume rate of oil flow is detected by the pads and it is the capacitances between pad and fixed disk (C_F) and between pad and self-aligning disk (C_S) which are measured.

Typical results are shown in Figs. 9.3 and 9.4. In Fig. 9.3 the disk–disk capacitance C_D and the pad–disk capacitance C_F are plotted as functions of the load. In Fig. 9.4 simultaneous measurements of C_F and C_D, similar to those of Fig. 9.3, are re-

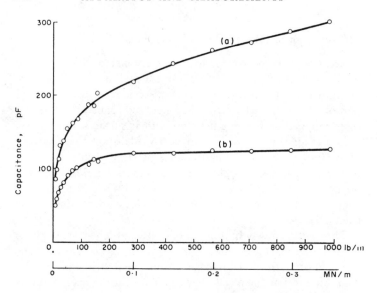

FIG. 9.3. Pad-disk capacitance and disk-disk capacitance as functions of load (peripheral speeds of both disks 6 m/s.) (a) Disk-disk capacitance. (b) Pad-disk capacitance.

[Reproduced from *Philosophical Transactions* Vol. A250, p. 387 (1958) by kind permission of The Royal Society.]

plotted, C_F being plotted as a function of C_D. It will be observed that the pattern of behaviour is as follows. At first C_D rises, reflecting a fall in film thickness with increasing load; C_F also rises proportionately (Fig. 9.4), reflecting the decreased volume rate of oil flow associated with the fall in film thickness (eqn. 9.1). At the heavier loads C_F is constant whereas C_D continues to increase with increasing loads; this suggests that the volume rate of oil flow (and therefore the film thickness at the pressure maximum) is constant but the increase in disk–disk capacitance with increasing load is due to deformation of the disks in the main load-bearing region.

Similar results were obtained in all experiments. It was always found that at the lighter loads C_F was proportional to C_D and,

TABLE 9.1. EXPERIMENTAL CONDITIONS

$(1 \times 10^4 \text{ N/m} = 57 \text{ lb/in.}; 1 \text{ m/s} \sim 200 \text{ ft/min})$

Conditions	u_2/u_1	$(u_2 - u_1)/\bar{u}$	range of load (10^4N/m)	limits of $\bar{u}$ (m/s)	limits of $(u_2 - u_1)$ (m/s)	limits of η_s (Pas)
Fig. 9.11 a	1·0	0	7 to 20	0·5 to 10	—	0·037 to 0·119
Fig. 9.11 b	1·5	0·40	5 to 20	0·32 to 7·5	0·13 to 3·0	0·013 to 0·104
Fig. 9.11 c	2·0	0·67	7 to 20	1·5 to 6·0	1·0 to 4·0	0·016 to 0·056
Fig. 9.11 d	2·5	0·86	7 to 20	1·4 to 5·6	1·2 to 4·8	0·014 to 0·054

as will be seen from the results given in Table 9.1, the constant of proportionality is independent of changes in the experimental conditions. From these results one can deduce the relation

$$C_r = 0.63C_D \qquad (9.2)$$

which applies to light loads when the disks are undeformed.

If the disks are undeformed it is a simple matter to calculate the theoretical value of the disk–disk capacitance. One obtains the result

$$C_D = 23.8h_0{}^{-\frac{1}{2}} \qquad (9.3)$$

In this calculation the dimensions of the disks used in the experiments have been used and it is also assumed that the gap

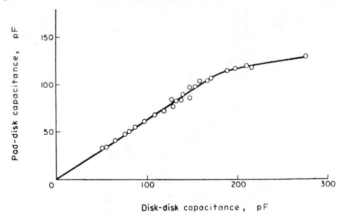

Fig. 9.4. Pad capacitance as a function of disk capacitance.

[Reproduced from *Philosophical Transactions* Vol. A250, p. 387 (1958) by kind permission of The Royal Society.]

between them is completely filled with oil having a dielectric constant of the measured value (2·30). Equation (9.3) contains h_0, the film thickness on the line of centres, whereas the volume rate of oil flow is associated with h_m the film thickness at the

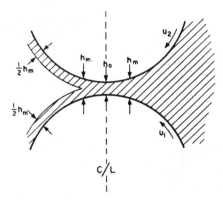

FIG. 9.5. Assumed disposition of the oil between the disks.
[Reproduced from *Philosophical Transactions* Vol. A250, p. 387
(1958) by kind permission of The Royal Society.]

pressure maximum. It will be assumed that the relationship between h_0 and h_m is that given by the cavitation criterion (see eqns. 3.10 and 3.18), i.e.

$$h_m = 1{\cdot}23h_0 \tag{9.4}$$

It is also inappropriate to assume that the gap between the disks is completely filled with oil. Instead it will be assumed that the oil is disposed as shown in Fig. 9.5 which is consistent with the assumptions of eqn. (9.4). One then obtains, instead of eqn. (9.3), the more appropriate relation

$$C_D = 0{\cdot}225h_m^{-1/2} \tag{9.5}$$

where C_D is in pico-farads when h_m is in metres.
Finally, combining eqns. (9.2) and (9.5) one obtains

$$C_F = 0{\cdot}142h_m^{-1/2}$$

or

$$h_m = 0{\cdot}0202/C_F^2 \tag{9.6}$$

From eqn. (9.6) it is possible to calculate the value of the film thickness at the pressure maximum h_m (in metres) from the measured value of the pad capacitance (in pico-farads). Although this calibration is based upon the behaviour of the system at light loads when the disks are undeformed it must apply also to higher loads. The capacitances of the pads are obviously determined by the volume rate of oil flow and the general validity of eqn. (9.1) ensures that the method is also applicable when the disks are deformed. However, since the pads detect the flow of uncompressed oil while the oil between the disks is compressed, some correction might be made to allow for this effect. The compressibilities of a wide range of lubricating oils are tabulated in a report of the A.S.M.E. (1953).

Finally it should be noted that the calibration of the pads given by eqn. (9.6) has been confirmed by two independent means. First the disposition of the oil beneath the pads has been observed directly by replacing the steel pads by glass plates. This method of calibration (Crook, 1958, Appendix) is less accurate than that given above but an equation similar to (9.6) was obtained with a somewhat higher constant of proportionality; within the estimated errors the agreement is satisfactory. Secondly it should be noted that the values of film thickness obtained using pads are in reasonable agreement with those obtained by other methods. A comparison of the results is shown in Fig. 9.9 and is discussed on page 153.

Measurement of the Shape of the Gap

The measurement of the shape of the gap allows the most complete comparison between theory and experiment to be made. The capacitance method of film thickness measurement has been extended by Crook (1961 c) to permit the measurement of the shape of the film and these measurements will now be outlined.

The four-disk machine (Fig. 9.2) was used under conditions near to the rolling point with the band brake, G, removed. Mercury contacts were fitted to permit electrical connections to both the central disk, D, and one of the outer disks. The central disk was of glass with a thin evaporated chronium electrode of the form shown in Fig. 9.6a to which the electrical connection was made. The three outer disks were of steel. The electrical connections were as shown in Fig. 9.6b. The leading edge of the

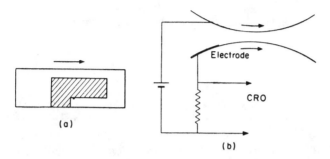

Fig. 9.6. Electrode arrangement for the measurement of oil film shape. (a) Plan of the chromium electrode. (b) The electrical circuit.

[Reproduced by kind permission from *Nature*, Vol. 190, p. 1182 (1961)].

electrode was arranged to be accurately aligned with a generator of the glass disk. As this leading edge of the electrode approaches and passes through the conjunction of the disks the capacitance rises. This capacitance is charged by a flow of current through the resistance R and, as shown below, the potential appearing across this resistance is proportional to ε/h where h is the film thickness and ε is the dielectric constant of the intervening medium. After suitable amplification this voltage is presented on a cathode-ray oscilloscope and can be photographed; a typical result is shown in Fig. 9.7. In this photograph the horizontal scale represents time, or distance in the x-direction, whilst the vertical scale represents the voltage across R or the local value of ε/h at each region of the gap. Both these scales can be calibrated by suitable external standards.

The theory of the method may be outlined briefly as follows. As the electrode moves through the gap the rate of change of capacitance is given by

$$\frac{dC}{dx} = \frac{\varepsilon L}{11\cdot3h} \times 10^{-10} \text{ F/m}$$

where L is the width of the leading edge of the electrode. Then

$$\frac{dC}{dt} = \frac{\varepsilon L u_1}{11\cdot3h} \times 10^{-10} \text{ F/s}$$

where u_1 is the peripheral speed of the glass disk. Provided that the time constant formed by the capacitance of the gap and the resistance R is suitably short, the current i flowing through R is $E\,dC/dt$, where E is the e.m.f. of the cell in the circuit. Then the voltage E_R across the resistance R is given as

$$E_R = \frac{ELu_1R}{11\cdot3} \times 10^{-10} \frac{\varepsilon}{h} \quad \text{V}$$

and when ε is taken as 2·3

$$E_k = 0\cdot2ELu_1R \times 10^{-10} h^{-1} \quad \text{V}$$

In Fig. 9.8 some oscilloscope traces have been transformed to give h as a function of x, (Crook, 1963). These demonstrate many of the salient features which have emerged from elasto-hydro-dynamic theory.

(1) The shape of the surfaces is nearly Hertzian.

(2) The film thickness is relatively insensitive to changes in the load; there is a small decrease with increasing load.

(3) The most significant departure from the Hertzian shape is a small constriction at recess. Under the more severe conditions this constriction leads to a local reduction in the film thickness of some 10–15 per cent.

(4) The film thickness (about 1 μm) is close to the value fore-cast by theory and to that obtained by other methods.

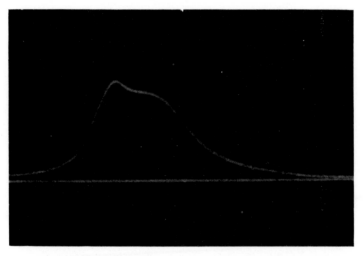

FIG. 9.7. Photograph from cathode ray oscilloscope trace.
[Reproduced by kind permission from *Nature*, **190,** 1182 (1961).]

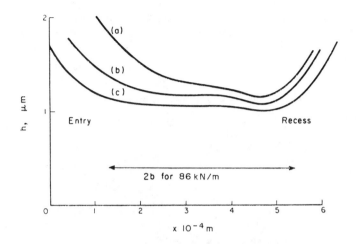

FIG. 9.8. Film profiles deduced from CRO traces. Peripheral speed
7·6 m/s. Loads (kN/m): (a) 39 (b) 64 (c) 86.

Comparison of Results Obtained by Different Methods

Although most of the results which will be described were
obtained using the pads it is relevant to show the close agreement between values of the film thickness obtained by the three
capacitance methods which have been outlined. This is illustrated in Fig. 9.9 in which the values of the film thickness, h,
are plotted against $u\eta_s$. The experimental points represent values
of h deduced from the total inter-specimen capacity (circles) and
from the experiments with a glass disk and evaporated metal
electrode (squares). The full line is drawn through all those
points which one would expect to be too low (by about 5 per cent)
because no allowance has been made for the small increase of
dielectric constant with pressure. The broken line represents the
best line through a much larger number of results obtained
using pads; one would expect these values to be too high (by
about 10 per cent) because no allowance has been made for the
fact that the oil between the disks is compressed whilst the pads
detect the flow of uncompressed oil. There is excellent agreement

between the results obtained by the different methods. The difference between the two lines of Fig. 9.9 (about 20 per cent) is close to that which is to be expected on account of the factors outlined above.

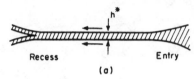

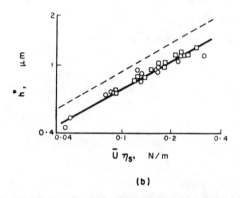

Fig. 9.9. Comparison of values of film thickness h obtained by different capacitance methods. (a) Oil filling between disks. (b) —○— from capacitance between steel disks. —□— from rate of change of capacitance between a steel disk and an electrode of evaporated chromium on a disk of glass. ——— from pad measurement with two-disk machine.

[Reproduced from *Philosophical Transactions* Vol. A255, p. 281 (1963) by kind permission of the Royal Society.]

The Controlling Viscosity

At an early stage of the experiments with the disk machines (Crook, 1957) it was noted that the lubricating oil formed films upon the disks; this oil was retained upon the surfaces and was only slowly replaced by fresh oil from the supply. It was also found (Crook, 1958) that if the oil supply was cut off the films of retained oil continued to lubricate the disks satisfactorily for a period of at least some 30 min. During this period the film thickness fell by about 30 per cent, but it was amply demonstrated that this fall was not caused by loss of oil from the retained film but was due to a rise in the temperature of the disks and the associated reduction in the viscosity of the oil. From

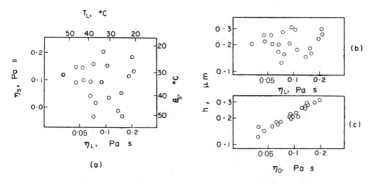

FIG. 9.10. Experiments to determine the controlling viscosity.
$R = 1.97$ cm $V = 0.93$ m/s.
[Reproduced from *Proceedings* Vol. A261, p. 532 (1961) by kind permission of the Royal Society.]

these and other experiments it became clear that the surface temperature of the specimens had a marked influence upon their lubrication.

During the experiments with the crossed-cylinders machine special precautions were adopted to control the temperature of the cylinders. Hollow specimens were used, through the bodies of which flowed streams of oil at a controlled temperature. In this way the specimen temperature (θ_s) could be maintained at a value significantly different from the temperature (θ_L) of the lubricating oil flowing to the surfaces. Experiments were performed in which both θ_s and θ_L were varied over a wide range; the purpose of these tests was to establish whether the film thickness h was controlled by η_s the viscosity of the oil at the specimen temperature (θ_s) or by η_L the viscosity of the lubricating oil as supplied to the system at a temperature (θ_L).

A set of experiments were chosen (Fig. 9.10a) in which there was no correlation between the values of η_L and η_s. The values of h deduced from these experiments show no significant correlation with η_L (Fig. 9.10b) whereas the correlation of h with η_s is highly significant. It is clear from these and other experiments that in considering the effect of viscosity upon film thickness it is the viscosity of the oil at the temperature of the specimens which is the controlling factor and that the temperature of the oil supply has no influence whatever, except insofar as it may affect the temperature of the apparatus. This finding is of some importance when it is realized that in earlier experiments the temperature of the specimens was rarely measured.

The results discussed above are readily understood in the light of the elasto-hydrodynamic theory outlined in the earlier part of this book. The theory shows that it is the properties of the oil (η_0, α) in the entry region which determine the value of the film thickness. Because the films are so thin, and because of the existence of the retained films, it is to be expected that the oil in the entry region will be in thermal equilibrium with the specimens, i.e. the η_0 of the theory is η_s, the viscosity of the oil at the temperature of the specimens. It should be noted that a theoretical analysis of the heat balance within the film (Crook, 1961b) has shown that the generation of heat from rolling or sliding friction will cause only small changes in temperature in the entry region. Within the range of conditions used in the experiments these temperature changes are so small that they have no significant influence upon the film thickness.

Experimental Values of the Film Thickness

An extensive series of experiments was performed using the two-disk machine (Fig. 9.1) in which the film thickness was measured using the pads. Various loads were used but all were sufficiently large to cause both deformation of the surfaces and the increase of viscosity with pressure; thus "full" elasto-hydro-dynamic theories such as those of Grubin were applicable to the conditions employed. The conditions are summarized in Table 9.1 (p. 147) and the results are plotted in Fig. 9.11.

Four series of experiments were performed with different proportions of rolling and sliding. The first series was performed under rolling conditions, $u_1 = u_2$, and in the subsequent series (u_1/u_2) had the values 1·5, 2·0 and 2·5. In Fig. 9.11a, which shows the results for rolling conditions, the full line represents the best line through the experimental points. This same line is plotted

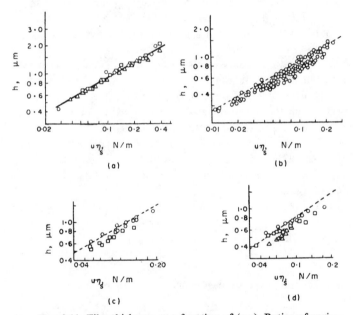

FIG. 9.11. Film thickness as a function of $(u\eta_s)$. Ratios of peripheral speeds (a) Rolling. (b) 1:1·5. (c) 1:2. (d) 1:2·5. In (a) (c) and (d) ○ indicates a load of $7·4 \times 10^4$ N/m, △ of $1·2 = \overline{1}0^5$ N/m, and □ a load of 2×10^5 N/m. In (b) loads are not identified but ranged from 5×10^4 to 2×10^5 N/m. (1×10^4 N/m = 57 lb/in.) — — — line of (a) superimposed.

as a broken line in Fig. 9.11 b, c and d which show values of the film thickness obtained when increasing proportions of sliding were introduced. A full analysis of the results is given in the original paper (Crook, 1961 a) but the major conclusions may be summarized as follows:

(a) When the values of film thickness as a function of $(u\eta_s)$ are plotted it is immediately apparent (see Fig. 9.11) that the introduction of sliding has little influence upon the film thickness. It is often suggested that sliding will reduce the film thickness because severe heating will cause a marked reduction of the viscosity of the oil in the pressure zone. Indeed in one series of experiments it was shown (using the methods described in Chapter 10) that under rolling conditions the average viscosity of the oil in the pressure zone was 60 Pas whilst the introduction of severe sliding reduced this viscosity to 1·4 Pas; however, despite this large reduction in the viscosity, the film thickness fell by only 10 per cent. As emphasized earlier, the reason for this result is that the film thickness is determined in the entry region where the oil is in temperature equilibrium with the specimens.

(b) As forecast by the theory, there is a small dependence of film thickness upon load but this reduction of h with increasing load is insignificant compared with the major dependence of h upon $(u\eta_s)$.

(c) Within ± 15 per cent all the results, regardless of variations with load or sliding, are expressed by

$$h = 2\cdot 5 \ (u\eta_s)^{0\cdot 5} \tag{9.7}$$

where h is the film thickness in microns, u is in m/s and η_s is in Pas.

In the study of point contacts (Archard and Kirk, 1961) the measurement of film thickness covered a wider range of some of the experimental variables. The temperature of the specimens was varied between 15 and 55 °C and although the major effect of this variation was to change the value of η_s (by a factor of approximately twelve) some account was taken of the small effect upon the value of α. In line with the simpler theories, it was assumed that h is a function of $(\alpha\eta_s)$. The radius of the specimens R was varied between 0·125 in. (3·2 mm) and 1·49 in. (3·77 cm) thus allowing an experimental measurement of the dependence of h upon R. The experiments covered a more than five hundredfold range of speeds and included speeds (equivalent values of u) of less than 1 cm/s. Under these conditions, where previously one would have assumed that only boundary lubrication was possible, it was shown that the films were a few hundred Angstrom units thick.

Statistical analysis of the point contact experiments gave the following results.

$$h = 0·44(\alpha\eta_s)^{0·57} u^{0·55} R^{0·62} \qquad (9.8)$$

where h is in metres, α in m²/N, η in Pas, u in m/s and R in m. It will be seen that the experimental dependence of h upon η_s and u is similar to that found in the experiments with line contacts (eqn. (9.7)). Moreover the values of film thickness obtained at a point contact are only about 40 per cent less than those obtained under corresponding conditions with a line contact.

For example, with 3 in. (76·2 mm) diameter disks and a value of $(u\eta_s)$ of 0·1 N/m the line contact experiments (eqn. 9.7), after allowing for the compressibility of the oil, gave a film thickness of about 0·7 μm. Under corresponding conditions the point contact experiments gave a film thickness of approximately 0·45 μm. There is thus a close similarity between the results obtained with the two different geometrical arrangements.

More recently, the experiments with the crossed-cylinders machine have been extended to include a wider range of materials (Archard and Kirk, 1963). Using specimens of brass and steel it was shown that small changes in the elastic modulus had no detectable influence upon the film thickness. When using specimens of glass and Perspex it was possible to observe directly the main load bearing region which, as forecast by the elasto-hydrodynamic theory, was found to have an area close to that deduced from Hertzian calculations. In experiments with Perspex specimens, values of the film thickness were deduced from observations of the white light interference fringes formed within the film (Kirk, 1962). These experiments with Perspex specimens showed that a large reduction in the elastic modulus changes radically the form of lubrication; the pressures are generally insufficient to increase the lubricant viscosity and, although the film thickness is comparable with that occurring between steel cylinders, the friction is an order of magnitude lower.

The experiments with the crossed-cylinders machine have also been extended to include a wider range of lubricants. An extensive series of measurements of film thicknesses were made with a range of hypoid oils using speeds between 0·007 m/s and 3·6 m/s and temperatures between 20 and 110°C (Archard, Hatcher and Kirk, 1964). When account is taken of the higher viscosity of the hypoid oils, these results were found to be in good agreement with the earlier experiments using an oil to Admiralty specification OM 100. It was shown that the addition of EP additives has no effect upon the thickness of the film. Some dozen lubricants of widely differing types have also been examined (Archard and Kirk, 1964); the experiments were performed at room temperature using a speed of 0·2 m/s. Most of these fluids gave values of the film thickness close to those predicted from the earlier work; the outstanding exceptions were silicone fluids for which the measured values were two or three orders of magnitude smaller than expected.

CHAPTER 10

FRICTION AND VISCOSITY

Theory

In the previous chapters the discussion of film thickness has been based upon isothermal conditions in the oil. It has been shown to a first approximation from experiment (Fig. 9.11) that, even when isothermal conditions no longer exist because of the introduction of sliding, the film thicknesses of pure rolling still prevail. But with respect to friction the isothermal assumption must be abandoned when sliding is introduced. Because sliding friction depends upon the actual viscosity of the oil separating the surfaces, because the actual viscosity will be affected by temperature, and because there must be a rise in temperature accompanying the work done in sliding against frictional resistance, it is apparent that the isothermal assumption will no longer suffice. Experimental results given later lead unequivocally to the same conclusion.

The temperature across the film is no longer constant so analysis must be based upon the Navier–Stokes equation in a form permitting viscosity (η) to vary with y as well as with x, i.e. upon

$$- \frac{\partial p}{\partial x} = \frac{\partial}{\partial y} \left(\eta \, \frac{\partial u}{\partial y} \right)$$

The coordinate system is shown in Fig. 10.1. The convention is that of the original papers (Crook, 1961b, 1963a) to which frequent reference will be made; it differs from the convention of the earlier chapters only in the assumed direction of u. Integration proceeds similarly to the integration of the isothermal equation. It is convenient to note the ordinate where $\partial u / \partial y = (u_2 - u_1)/h$; that ordinate will be denoted by $y = h/n$ and the viscosity at that ordinate by η_n. The integration then gives (Crook, 1961 b)

$$\frac{\partial u}{\partial y} = -\frac{1}{\eta} \frac{\partial p}{\partial x} \left[y - \frac{h}{n} \right] + \frac{\eta_n}{\eta} \frac{(u_2 - u_1)}{h} \qquad (10.1)$$

which reduces to the isothermal result when $n = 2$ and when, as by assumption η_n is indistinguishable from η. (There are two values of y at which $\partial u / \partial y = (u_2 - u_1)/h$; at $y = h/n$ and $y = h(1 - (1/n))$. Results are the same which ever is taken.)

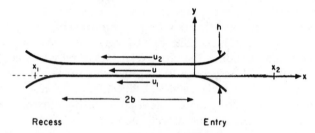

FIG. 10.1. Coordinates.

[Reproduced from *Philosophical Transactions* Vol. A255, p. 281 (1963) by kind permission of The Royal Society.]

The frictional tractions per unit face width at each surface (F_1 and F_2) are given by

$$F_1 = -\int_{x_1}^{x_2} \left(\eta \frac{\partial u}{\partial y} \right)_{y=0} dx \quad \text{and} \quad F_2 = \int_{x_1}^{x_2} \left(\eta \frac{du}{dy} \right)_{y=h} dx$$

where the interval x_2 to x_1 embraces the region of any significant friction (Fig. 10.1). From eqn. (10.1) it follows that

$$\left. \begin{aligned} F_1 &= -\int_{x_1}^{x_2} \frac{h}{n} \frac{\partial p}{\partial x} dx - (u_2 - u_1) \int_{x_1}^{x_2} \frac{\eta_n}{h} dx, \\ F_2 &= -\int_{x_1}^{x_2} h \left(1 - \frac{1}{n} \right) \frac{\partial p}{\partial x} dx + (u_2 - u_1) \int_{x_1}^{x_2} \frac{\eta_n}{h} dx \end{aligned} \right\} \qquad (10.2)$$

In both instances the first integral can be identified with the rolling friction as it remains when $u_1 = u_2$. The second integral is the sliding component of the friction.

It will help to make clear what follows to note that at loads where the oil film develops a parallel section of approximately Hertzian width ($2b$) the rolling friction pertains almost entirely to the entry region of the parallel film. The reasons why this should be so will emerge later. Furthermore, only loads at which the film has a parallel section will be considered.

For such loads and at speeds of sliding above a few cm/sec the sliding component predominates and the rolling component can be ignored. Then the term in $\partial p/\partial x$ of eqn. (10.1) may also be ignored and it follows that

$$\int_0^h \frac{\partial u}{\partial y}\, \mathrm{d}y = (u_2 - u_1) = \frac{\eta_n(u_2 - u_1)}{h} \int_0^h \frac{\mathrm{d}y}{\eta}$$

so

$$\frac{1}{\eta_n} = \frac{1}{h}\int_0^h \frac{\mathrm{d}y}{\eta} \qquad (10.3)$$

This conclusion and eqn. (10.2) will be referred to later.

The Heat Balance

The heat generated within the oil film will be carried away both by conduction across the film to the metal surfaces and by transport with the oil as it moves through the conjunction. The latter will be called convection.

The rate of generation of heat per unit volume is given by the product of stress and rate of strain, i.e. by

$$q = \eta \left(\frac{\partial u}{\partial y}\right)^2$$

and ignoring the term in $\partial p/\partial x$ of eqn. (10.1)

$$q = \frac{\eta_n^2}{\eta} \frac{(u_2 - u_1)^2}{h^2}$$

The rate at which heat is carried away is given by

$$\varrho cu \frac{\partial \theta}{\partial x} + k \frac{\partial^2 \theta}{\partial y^2} = -q \qquad (10.4)$$

where θ is temperature and ϱ, c and k are respectively the density, specific heat and thermal conductivity of the oil. It will be assumed that the surfaces of the metal are isothermal surfaces at temperature θ_s; this is not strictly so but the error due to the assumption is small (Crook, 1961 b). The symbol θ will denote, with reference to θ_s, the rise in temperature at a point in the film.

No way has been found of solving eqn. (10.4) by analytical methods with both terms on the left retained simultaneously, but the equations

$$\varrho cu \frac{\partial \theta}{\partial x} = -q, \quad k \frac{\partial^2 \theta}{\partial y^2} = -q$$

have both been discussed (Crook, 1961 b) and it has been shown that over the region in which the film is parallel the former equation leads to values of θ greatly exceeding those given by the latter. This implies that conduction is dominant and therefore only the equation

$$k \frac{\partial^2 \theta}{\partial y^2} = -q = \frac{-\eta_n^2}{\eta} \frac{(u_2 - u_1)^2}{h^2} \qquad (10.5)$$

will be considered here.

The temperature θ must be symmetrical with respect to $y = h/2$ and by taking this together with eqn. (10.3) into account it follows from integration of eqn. (10.5) with respect to y that

$$\left(\frac{\partial \theta}{\partial y}\right)^2_{y=0,h} = \frac{\eta_n^2}{4k^2} \frac{(u_2 - u_1)^4}{h^2} \qquad (10.6)$$

If η is expressed in terms of θ, eqn. (10.5) can again be integrated. It will be assumed that

$$\eta = \eta_x \exp(-\gamma\theta)$$

where η_x is the viscosity at the surfaces, i.e. at temperature θ_s and at the pressure appropriate to the associated value of x. Integration of eqn. (10.5) then gives

$$\left(\frac{\partial \theta}{\partial y}\right)^2 = 2\omega\left[1 - \frac{A}{\gamma\omega}\exp(\gamma\theta)\right], \quad A = \frac{\eta_n^2}{k\eta_x}\frac{(u_2 - u_1)^2}{h^2} \tag{10.7}$$

where ω is a constant of integration. By comparing the two expressions for $\left(\dfrac{\partial \theta}{\partial y}\right)^2_{y=0,h}$ from eqns. (10.6) and (10.7) it follows that

$$\omega = \frac{8\eta_n^2\psi(\psi + 1)}{\eta_x^2 h^2 \psi^2}, \quad \psi = \frac{\eta_x\gamma(u_2 - u_1)^2}{8k} \tag{10.8}$$

It also follows from eqn. (10.7) that if θ_c is the rise in temperature from either surface of $y = h/2$ that

$$\exp(\gamma\theta_c) = \gamma\omega/A = (\psi + 1) \tag{10.9}$$

A further integration of eqn. (10.7) with the boundary condition $y = 0$, $\theta = 0$ gives for the interval $0 \leqq y \leqq h/2$

$$\ln\left[\frac{1 - [1 - \exp(\gamma\theta - \gamma\theta_c)]^{1/2}}{1 + [1 - \exp(\gamma\theta - \gamma\theta_c)]^{1/2}}\right]$$

$$- \ln\left[\frac{1 - [1 - \exp(-\gamma\theta_c)]^{1/2}}{1 + [1 - \exp(-\gamma\theta_c)]^{1/2}}\right] = y\gamma\sqrt{2\omega}$$

The first term on the left is zero when $y = h/2$ as then $\theta = \theta_c$ so

$$\omega = \frac{2}{h^2\gamma^2}\left[\ln\left\{\frac{1 - [1 - \exp(-\gamma\theta_c)]^{1/2}}{1 + [1 - \exp(-\gamma\theta_c)]^{1/2}}\right\}\right]^2 \tag{10.10}$$

From a comparison of eqns. (10.8) and (10.9) it follows that

$$\eta_n = \eta_x f(\psi), \quad f(\psi) = \frac{\ln\left\{(\psi + 1)^{1/2} + \sqrt{\psi}\right\}}{[\psi(\psi + 1)]^{1/2}} \tag{10.11}$$

Consequently, both the temperature on the median plane (θ_c) and η'' are determined by the number ψ. A graph of $f(\psi)$ is given in Fig. 10.2 and in addition a graph of the approximation

$$f(\psi) \approx \ln (4\psi)/2\psi \qquad (10.12)$$

which is valid for $\psi \gg 1$.

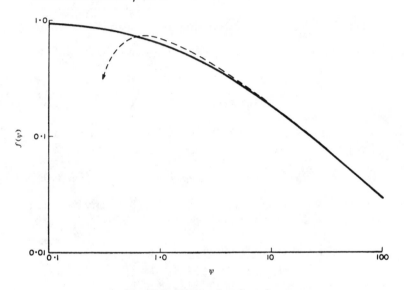

FIG. 10.2. $f(\psi)$ as a function of ψ.

[Reproduced from *Philosophical Transactions* Vol. A254, p. 237 (1961) by kind permission of The Royal Society.]

Sliding Friction and Effective Viscosity

If F_s is the frictional traction due to sliding per unit face width it follows from eqn. (10.2) that

$$F_s = (u_2 - u_1) \int_{x_1}^{x_2} \frac{\eta_n}{h} \, dx$$

To a sufficient accuracy the limits x_1 and x_2 can be identified with the limits of the Hertzian zone ($x = -2b$, 0) over which the film has a constant thickness h^*. It follows that

$$F_s = \frac{(u_2 - u_1)}{h^*} \int_{-2b}^{0} \eta_n \, dx \qquad (10.13)$$

If an effective viscosity ($\overline{\eta}_n$) is defined as that constant viscosity which would give rise to the frictional traction F_s then

$$F_s = \frac{2\overline{\eta}_n b(u_2 - u_1)}{h^*} \qquad (10.14)$$

and it follows from eqns. (10.13) and (10.14) that

$$\overline{\eta}_n = \frac{1}{2b} \int_{-2b}^{0} \eta_n \, dx \qquad (10.15)$$

To evaluate $\overline{\eta}_n$ from eqns. (10.11) and (10.15) η_x must be expressed in terms of pressure. It will be assumed that

$$\eta_x = \eta_s \exp \alpha p \qquad (10.16)$$

where η_s is the viscosity of the oil at the temperature of the surfaces (θ_s) and at zero pressure. (It is unnecessary to make a distinction between atmospheric and zero pressure.)

It is now possible to calculate both $\overline{\eta}_n$ and F_s (eqn. (10.14)) in terms of h^* and sliding speed. For values of $\psi \gg 1$ the approximation of eqn. (10.12) is valid. For a Hertzian pressure distribution together with $\psi \gg 1$ eqn. (10.15) can be integrated analytically when it is found that

$$\overline{\eta}_n \approx \frac{4k}{b\gamma(u_2 - u_1)^2} \times$$
$$\times \left[\frac{1}{2} \alpha w + 2b \ln (u_2 - u_1) + b \ln \left(\frac{\eta_s \gamma}{2k} \right) \right] (10.17)$$

where w is the load per unit face width. For values of ψ too small for the approximation of eqn. (10.12) to be valid, $\overline{\eta}_n$ and F_s can be calculated by numerical integration.

In the entry zone h is large compared with h^* and, because the pressures are low, η_n is small. A consequence is that the entry zone makes only a small contribution to the sliding friction in comparison with that of the Hertzian zone.

The Rolling Friction

By symmetry $n = 2$ when the surfaces roll and the rolling friction is given from eqns. (10.2) by

$$F_R = -\frac{1}{2}\int_{x_1}^{x_2} h \, \frac{\partial p}{\partial x} \, dx$$

The reader is referred to the original paper (Crook, 1963a) for the evaluation of F_R but the point will be made that the integral can be expressed in the form

$$\int p \, \frac{\partial h}{\partial x} \, dx$$

when it becomes evident that the region in which h is constant can make no contribution to the rolling friction. It follows that rolling friction arises predominantly in the entry zone.

By taking an approximate expression for the shape of the entry zone together with Grubin's method of expressing p an expression for F_R can be developed (Crook, 1963a). It is found that the rolling friction is proportional to h^*.

Experimental Results and Their Comparison With Theory. High Speeds of Sliding

Results for speeds of sliding so high that temperature effects are marked will be considered first.

The basic experimental data consists of measurements of friction, film thickness and disk temperature (θ_s) obtained with the two-disk machine of Fig. 9.1. From the measurements of friction and film thickness experimental values of $\bar{\eta}_n$ were deduced (eqn. (10.14)).

In Fig. 10.3 some experimental values of friction are given. The friction is given as a function of sliding speed for three different loads. The experiments were arranged so that the rolling speed $((u_2 + u_1)/2)$ was held constant at 4 m/s as the sliding speed $(u_2 - u_1)$ was varied. The frictional traction fell with the

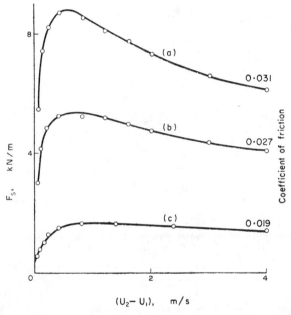

FIG. 10.3. Frictional traction as a function of sliding speed. (Rolling speed constant at 4 m/s). Load (10^4 N/m: (a) 20 (b) 15 (c) 7·5.

[Reproduced from *Philosophical Transactions* Vol. A255, p. 281 (1963) by kind permission of The Royal Society.]

load and at constant load it reached a maximum and then fell as the sliding speed was increased. In Fig. 10.4 some further results are given. Here the load was constant and for curves a, b, c and e the values of η_s was also constant (0·04 Pas) but for each curve a different rolling speed was taken. As the rolling speed increased the friction fell. The conditions of curves c and d were the same except that the value of η_s for curve d was 0·07 Pas instead of 0·04 Pas. Although the higher value of η_s gave a greater friction initially, ultimately it gave the lower friction as the sliding speed increased. This is important. It implies that if

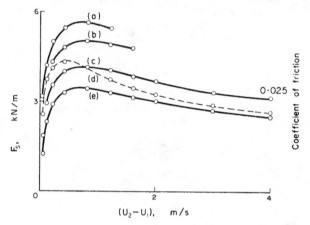

FIG. 10.4. Frictional traction as a function of the speed of sliding
Load $1·25 \times 10^5$ N/m.   (a) $U = 1·2$ m/s, $\eta_s \simeq 0·04$ Pas.
(b) $U = 2$ m/s, $\eta_s \simeq 0·04$ Pas. (c) $U = 4$ m/s, $\eta_s \simeq 0·04$ Pas.
(d) $U = 4$ m/s, $\eta_s \simeq 0·07$ Pas. (e) $U = 6$ m/s, $\eta_s \simeq 0·04$ Pas.

[Reproduced from *Philosophical Transactions* Vol. A255, p. 281 (1963) by kind permission of the Royal Society.]

η_s is increased to give to the surfaces the greater protection of a thicker film then, provided that the sliding speed is sufficiently high, this will not carry the disadvantage of a greater friction.

In Fig. 10.5 some calculated frictional tractions are given. The curves again exhibit a lower final friction for a greater η_s (curves b and c). Furthermore, it is evident from eqn. (10.14) that, like the experimental curves of Fig. 10.4 calculated curves of friction must show a friction which falls as the rolling speed is increased because, for constant η_s the film thickness (h^*) will become greater as the rolling speed is increased. The calculated curves are therefore qualitatively similar to the experimental curves but the calculated curves rise to sharper and higher peaks than the comparable experimental curves (cf. curve a of Fig. 10.5 and curve a of Fig. 10.3).

In Fig. 10.6 a comparison is shown of experimental and calculated values of $\bar{\eta}_n$. In the figure $\bar{\eta}_n$ is given, for various values of load and rolling speed, as a function of sliding speed. Near the rolling point the high values of $\bar{\eta}_n$ are due to the effect of pressure upon viscosity. As sliding is introduced the temperatures developed within the oil film depress $\bar{\eta}_n$ and it should be noted that a depression of about two decades occurred when the sliding speed reached 4 m/s.

There is a closer agreement between the experimental and calculated curves for $\bar{\eta}_n$ than between those for friction. This is because the calculated curves for $\bar{\eta}_n$ are based upon values of α and k/γ (see eqn. 10.17) derived from the experimental results whereas the calculated frictions are based upon values derived from published results of measurements at higher pressures in

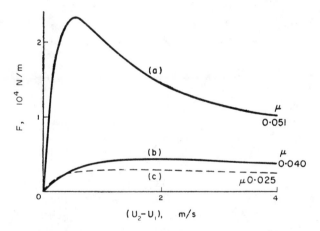

FIG. 10.5. Calculated frictional traction as a function of sliding speed. (a) $w = 2 \times 10^5$ N/m, $\eta_s = 0.04$ Pas. (b) $w = 1 \times 10^5$ N/m, $\eta_s = 0.04$ Pas. (c) $w = 1 \times 10^5$ N/m, $\eta_s = 0.1$ Pas.

[Reproduced from *Philosophical Transactions* Vol. A254, p. 237 (1961) by kind permission of The Royal Society.]

apparatus following Bridgman (1949). Published results are not available for the actual oil of the disk experiments but more importantly the high pressure measurements give equilibrium values whereas in the disk experiments values should be appropriate to the transient stress experienced by the oil as it passes through the pressure zone. There is a difference and until values independently obtained become available, values derived from the results of the disk experiments must perforce be used. The values of k/γ used in calculating the curves ranged from 1·3 to 1·8 N/s and the values of a ranged from 1·95 to 1·43 × 10⁻⁸ m²/N.

It is noticeable that the calculated curves depart from the experimental curves (Fig. 10.6) at low values of sliding speed; this

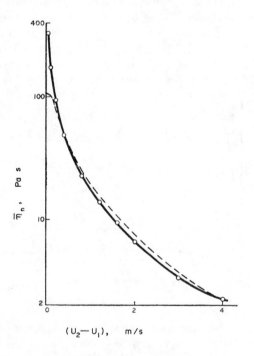

FIG. 10.6. (a) Effective viscosity as a function of sliding speed. Load = 7·5 × 10⁴ N/m.   U = 4 m/s, $\eta_s \simeq$ 0·04 Pas.   —O— experimental. — — — calculated.

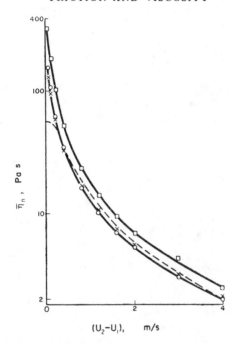

FIG. 10.6. (b) Load $= 1.25 \times 10^5$ N/m. Experimental O,
$U = 4$ m/s, $\eta_s \simeq 0.04$ Pas$\times$, $U = 6$ m/s, $\eta_s \simeq 0.04$ Pas.$\square$
$U = 4$ m/s, $\eta_s \simeq 0.07$ Pas. — — — calculated for $\eta_s = 0.04$ Pas.

is another manifestation of the fact noted previously that the calculated frictions rise to higher and sharper peaks than those found experimentally. By taking values of k/γ both implausibly large and small it was established (Crook, 1963a) that the sharp fall in $\bar{\eta}_n$ with sliding speed exhibited by the experimental curves at small speeds of sliding cannot be explained in terms of temperature. It is concluded that in addition to temperature effects there is an intrinsic effect of shear rate upon the viscosity of the oil.

The theory of the heat balance within the oil film accounts satisfactorily for many of the observations and in particular for the larger phenomena. It is essential for progress into an under-

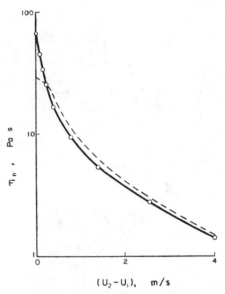

FIG. 10.6 (c) Load $= 2 \times 10^5$ N/m. $U = 4$ m/s, $\eta_s \simeq 0.04$ Pas
—O— experimental, — — — calculated.

[Reproduced from *Philosophical Transactions* Vol. A255, p. 281 (1963) by kind permission of The Royal Society.]

standing of the rheological behaviour of oils in elasto-hydro-dynamics that the behaviour attributable to the heat balance should first be known.

Rolling Friction and Results of Low Speeds of Sliding

The results now to be described were obtained with the four disk machine of Fig. 9.2. The principle of operation of this machine has been given in Chapter 9.

The experimental data comprised measurements of sliding speed between the inner and outer disks for various values of braking torque applied to the inner disk. A stroboscope lamp triggered from the driving shaft was used to measure the sliding speed. The disk temperature was also measured. In addition, in separate experiments measurements of capacitance were made. These measurements showed that the thickness of the oil film at each of the three conjunctions of the four-disk machine agreed, within the limits of experimental error, with the film thickness given by the two-disk machine when run in a corresponding condition.

In Fig. 10.7 some typical measurements of friction as a function of sliding speed are given. The experimental method deter-

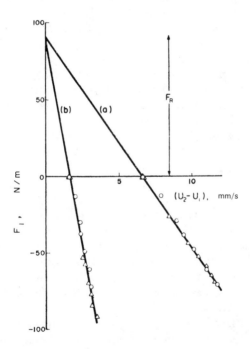

FIG. 10.7. Surface traction (F_1) as a function of sliding speed. (F_R is the rolling friction.) (a) Load $= 7.4 \times 10^4$ N/m, $U =$ 2.6 m/s, $\eta_s = 0.042$ Pas. (b) Load $= 2 \times 10^5$ N/m, $U = 3$ m/s, $\eta_s = 0.04$ Pas $\bigcirc$ and $\triangle$ differentiate directions of rotation.

(Reproduced from *Philosophical Transactions* Vol. A255, p. 281 (1963) by kind permission of The Royal Society.]

mines that it is the friction of the surface of lower speed which is known (F_1). This friction is given by

$$F_1 = F_R - F_S = F_R - \frac{2\bar{\eta}_n b(u_2 - u_1)}{h^*}$$

Therefore the intercept of lines through the experimental points with the friction axis gives the rolling friction.

The rolling friction was determined for various loads and for various combinations of η_s and rolling speed $(u = (u_1 + u_2)/2)$. It was found that the rolling friction is independent of load and proportional to $(u\eta_s)^{1/2}$ (Fig. 10.8a). It follows that the rolling friction is proportional to h^* (Fig. 10.8b) as h^* is also proportional to $(u\eta_s)^{1/2}$ (Chapter 9). In this respect there is, therefore, agreement between the experimental results and the theory of rolling friction which has been referred to earlier. Furthermore it has been established that a satisfactory agreement exists between the experimentally determined and calculated constants of proportionality (Crook, 1963a).

Values of $\bar{\eta}_n$ were calculated from the rate of change of friction with sliding speed and the known film thickness. Because it can be shown from the theory of the heat balance that the rise in temperature within the oil film is negligible for the sliding speeds of a few cm/sec employed, these values of $\bar{\eta}_n$ display the effect of pressure upon oil viscosity without modification by heating of the oil within the conjunction. Absence of heating is confirmed by the fact that the experimental points lie on straight lines whereas if the viscosity was being modified by frictional heat, the lines would curve towards the horizontal as the sliding speed increased; i.e. as the viscosity became more depressed by greater frictional heat.

In Fig. 10.9 the ratio $\bar{\eta}_n/\eta_s$ is plotted as a function of rolling speed $(\bar{u})$ for various loads. This ratio was formed to remove from consideration the proportional influence of η_s upon $\bar{\eta}_n$ and to give a quantity most dependent upon pressure alone. Nevertheless it can be seen from the solid and interrupted curves of the figure for a load of 7.4×10^4 N/m that some dependence upon η_s remains.

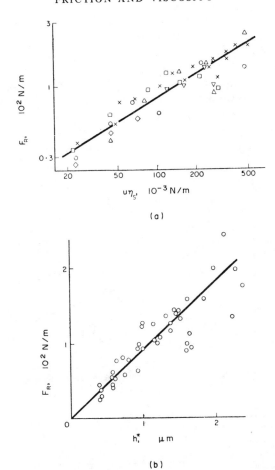

FIG. 10.8. Rolling friction in relation to $u\eta_s$ and film thickness.
(a) F_R as a function of $u\eta_s$. Load$(10^4$ N/m).$\diamond$ 2·5, $\circ$ 4·9, $\times$ 7·4,
$\square$ 10·0, $\triangle$ 14·6,   19·7. $(2\times10^5$ N/m = 1120 lb/in.) (b) F_R as a
function of film thickness. (Same results as for (a)).

[Reproduced from *Philosophical Transactions* Vol. A255, p. 281
(1963) by kind permission of The Royal Society.]

The figure confirms that the viscosity of oil is dependent upon pressure; at the highest load the figure shows an increase in viscosity by a factor of 1×10^5. Such an increase is to be expected from measurements which have been made of the viscosity of oils when under high pressure (A.S.M.E., 1953). But in addition the figure shows that pressure becomes less effective in raising viscosity as the rolling speed is increased; that could not be found from previous measurements at high pressure in which viscosity was measured under conditions of sustained stress.

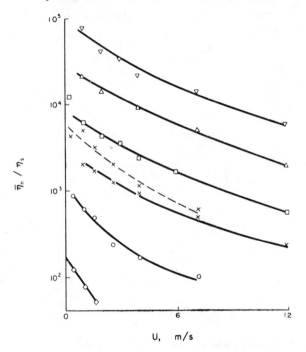

FIG. 10.9. The ratio $\bar{\eta}_n/\eta_s$ in pure rolling. Load (10^4 N/m)
$\diamondsuit$ 2·5, $\bigcirc$ 4·9, $\times$ 7·4, $\square$ 10, $\triangleleft$ 14·6, $\triangle$ 19·7, ——— 0·02 Pas
$< \eta_s < 0·06$ Pas. — — — 0·06 Pas. $< \eta_s < 0·15$ Pas. (10 m/s.
= 1980 ft/min).

However, at zero rolling speed the results from the disk machine should coincide with the results for a sustained stress. The comparison cannot be made straightforwardly because the A.S.M.E. Report (1953) does not include results for the oil of the disk machine experiments, and because the results of the Report for an oil, near in specification to that oil were not carried up to such high viscosities. Therefore a comparison requires an extrapolation of the results of the Report. But within these limitations agreement exists (Crook, 1962). The variation of the effect of pressure upon viscosity with rolling speed can be expressed as a variation of α (eqn. 10.16) with rolling speed. Values of α are given in Fig. 10.10 from which it can be seen that α also varies with load and with η_s, i.e. with θ_s. It is a consequence of the reduction of α as the rolling speed increases that film thickness will increase less rapidly with rolling speed than the increase predicted when a constant value of α is assumed. The variation of α

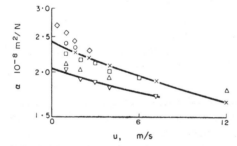

FIG. 10.10. The variation of α with rolling speed. 0·035 Pas $< \eta_s <$ 0·045 Pas, Load (10^4 N/m) O 4·9, × 7·4, □ 10·0, △ 14·6, ▽ 19·7. 0·11 Pas $< \eta_s <$ 0·143 Pas, Load (10^4 N/m) ◇ 7·4.

[Reproduced from *Philosophical Transactions* Vol. A255, p. 281 (1963) by kind permission of The Royal Society.]

with rolling speed therefore accounts, at least in part, for the fact that theory predicts a film thickness varying with $\bar{u}\eta_s$ raised approximately to a power of 0·7 whereas experiment gives an exponent of 0·5 (Fig. 9.11).

Because, under the conditions of the experiments, any rise of temperature within the oil is negligible, the temperature of the oil at all points within the film was uniform and coincident with θ_s. Consequently, by making measurements at various values of θ_s the effect of temperature upon a viscosity enhanced by pressure can be investigated. Appropriate measurements were made and some results are summarized in Fig. 10.11 where $\gamma(\eta_{\theta_2} = \eta_{\theta_1} \exp -\gamma(\theta_2 - \theta_1))$ is plotted against rolling speed.

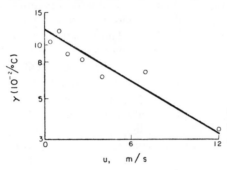

FIG. 10.11. The variation of γ with rolling speed. (Load $= 7\cdot4 \times 10^4$ N/m).

[Reproduced from *Philosophical Transactions* Vol. A255, p. 281 (1963) by kind permission of The Royal Society.]

From the variation of γ it is seen that viscosity becomes less sensitive to changes in temperature as the rolling speed increases.

Therefore, the dependence of viscosity or, more properly, of the apparent viscosity of oil upon both pressure and temperature becomes less marked as the rolling speed increases, becomes less marked as the time of transit of the oil through the conjunction is reduced. The term "apparent viscosity" should be stressed. The primary observation is frictional traction. That traction has been interpreted in terms of viscosity but probably other rheological factors contribute to it.

A greater accumulation of evidence than is available at the time of writing is required for a definitive identification of the additional rheological factors. But the influence of time upon the effects of pressure and temperature can be accounted for, although tentatively, in a semi-quantitative manner by assuming that the oil possesses shear elasticity in addition to viscosity, i.e. is a Maxwellian fluid. If the oil possesses elasticity the relative motion of the surface of one disk with respect to the other will be greater than that due solely to the viscosity of the oil. Consequently if the observed relative motion is interpreted in terms of viscosity alone, the apparent viscosity so obtained will be less than the actual viscosity.

If the time of transit is long the elastic contribution becomes an insignificant part of the total relative motion. It can be shown that it becomes significant at times of transit equal to or less than the *relaxation time* of the oil. The relaxation time is the time required for the stress associated with a suddenly imposed shear strain to fall to $1/e$ of its initial value and is defined by η/G where η is the true viscosity of the oil and G is its elastic shear modulus. When interpreted in terms of visco-elasticity the experimental results imply that the oil has a relaxation time of the order 1×10^{-4} sec. For a further discussion the reader is referred to the original paper (Crook, 1963a).

Experiments with disk machines have covered a wide range of purposes. The first experiments were conducted solely with the object of predicting the maximum conditions of speed and load at which gear teeth would operate without damage to the tooth surfaces. At that time the existence of a hydrodynamic film, although not unsuspected, was not widely recognized. Through disk machine experiments the existence of a hydrodynamic film was brought to the forefront and knowledge of the thickness of the hydrodynamic film was obtained. Now, in addition, the disk machine can be seen as an instrument for study of the rheological properties of oils in conditions of high pressure and transient stress.

CHAPTER 11

COMPARISON OF THEORY
AND EXPERIMENT

THE limited, but rigorous, numerical analysis of the elasto-hydrodynamic problem has been concerned primarily with the pressure distribution and the film geometry in a lubricated contact, and to a lesser extent with the elastic stresses in the solids and the viscous forces on the surfaces of the solids. Valuable examinations of the thermal effects which play a part in contact phenomena (Crook, 1961 b; Merritt, 1962) have been approximate in nature. Experiments have concentrated largely on the measurement of film thickness, film shape and friction. The only quantity, therefore, which has attracted the detailed attention of both experiment and independent analysis is *film geometry*. This, and in particular the minimum film thickness, will occupy most of the discussion in this chapter. But first we shall take a look at some of the interesting experiments which lie on the fringe of our direct comparison between theory and experiment.

The extensive investigation of nominal point contacts by Archard and Kirk (1961), briefly described in Chapter 9, reveals an elasto-hydrodynamic regime over a wide range of conditions where previously it had been assumed that only boundary lubrication could occur. Moreover the film thicknesses at point contacts are surprisingly close to those in the corresponding line contact situation.

The *normal approach* of two cylindrical surfaces separated by a lubricant has received the detailed theoretical attention of Christensen (1962). An experiment roughly related to the theory qualitatively confirmed the prediction that a very high pressure peak may be developed in the lubricating film, much higher than the Hertzian dry contact pressure. An interesting point in common with the theory of rolling contact is that the value of the maximum pressure reached depends to a large extent on the value of the parameter $\alpha E'$.

Direct pressure measurements, in situations where elastohydrodynamic effects are important, have so far been restricted to experiments whose physical conditions are far removed from

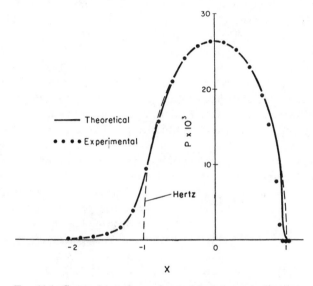

Fig. 11.1. Comparison of experimental and theoretical pressure distributions for 12 lb/in. load. Rubber block experiment. [Reproduced from the *International Journal of Mechanical Science*, Vol. 4, pp. 205–10 (1962) by kind permission of Pergamon Press.]

engineering reality. The difficulties in making direct pressure measurements in a realistic contact are considerable; a point on the surface of the solids moves fast through a zone of high pressure which is less than a mm wide and where the oil film thickness is only about 1 μm. Two experiments have been reported in which pressure measurements were taken. In both of these the solids were in nominal line contact and the motion involved considererable sliding, one solid being stationary in each case. Unfortunately, in both experiments, conditions were such that, theoretically, no secondary peak in the pressure distribution was to be expected. In the first (Higginson, 1962) a large zone width was obtained at low pressures by using a block of rubber as the stationary solid. The pressure was measured through a small hole in the rubber with a simple manometer. The pressure were so low and the temperature variation sō small that the oil viscosity was sensibly constant at its bulk value. However the results were entirely in harmony with elasto-hydro-dynamic theory. In particular two results are shown in Figs. 8.13 and 11.1. In Fig. 8.13 pressure distributions are recorded for a range of loads at constant speed. It is interesting to compare the development of the Hertzian form of pressure as the load increases with the qualitatively corresponding theoretical result shown in Fig. 7.2. Figure 11.1 shows in dimensionless terms one of these pressure curves and the corresponding theoretical solution. The second of these experiments (Dowson and Longfield, 1963b) was slightly more realistic, although still very unlike a machine contact. In this experiment a large zone width was achieved in a metal to metal contact by using mating cylindrical surfaces of high geometrical conformity. Some of the results have been given in Chapter 8; although a direct comparison with the theory cannot be made, qualitatively the results are quite consistent with its predictions.

Film Thickness and Shape

We turn now to film thickness, which has been measured in metal to metal contacts over a wide range of conditions corresponding to those arising in practice. The outstanding measurements in nominal line contacts are those of Crook in this country and Sibley and Orcutt in the U.S.A.; Crook's are of centre-line film thickness and Sibley and Orcutt's presumably of minimum film thickness. Actually the latter experiments were conducted on a disk machine whose disks were slightly crowned, giving a long elliptical contact.

A large sample of Sibley and Orcutt's results is compared with the theoretical formula (7.1) in Fig. 11.2; a fair selection from these, including extreme values, is given in detail in Table 11.1. In the experiments load, speed, viscosity and pressure-viscosity

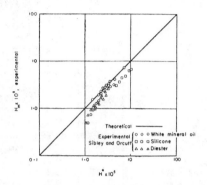

FIG. 11.2. Comparison of H^* with experimental H_m
(Sibley and Orcutt).

index were varied. In calculating the equivalent load per unit width, Sibley and Orcutt allowed for the slight crowning on their disks; their values of equivalent load have been used in calculating H^* in Fig. 11.2, and since the effect of load on H^* is small it is unlikely that other interpretations of the effective load would give appreciably different results. It should be noted, however, that the variation of the measured film thickness with load, although slight, is somewhat greater than the theory suggests. A notable feature of Fig. 11.2 is the similarity in slope between the experimental results and the theory. Indeed, overall, the agreement between these experiments and the theory is very good. At very small film thicknesses the experimental values fall markedly below the theoretical line. It is to be expected that the X-ray transmission technique will underestimate the effective film thickness between surfaces which are not smooth, and this

TABLE 11.1. SELECTION OF FILM THICKNESSES MEASURED BY
SIBLEY AND ORCUTT

Lubricant	Viscosity at mean disc temperature 10^{-3} Pa s	Pressure Viscosity Coefficient 10^{-9}m^2/N	Load per unit width MN/m	Disc rolling speed m/s	Minimum film thickness μm	
					Experi-mental	Theor-etical
White mineral oil	9·1	9·3	0·227	13·2	0·41	0·38
			0·341	8·8	0·28	0·25
				13·2	0·41	0·41
				22·2	0·58	0·58
			0·819	8·8	0·18	0·28
				11·1	0·23	0·33
				13·2	0·28	0·35
Diester	9·7	8·7	0·341	8·8	0·23	0·30
				13·2	0·33	0·43
				22·2	0·48	0·61
			0·819	13·2	0·23	0·38
				22·2	0·33	0·53
Diester	6·2	8·0	0·341	13·2	0·23	0·28
				22·2	0·30	0·41
Silicone	23·4	22	0·341	13·2	1·30	1·32
			0·819	8·8	0·58	0·89
				13·2	0·82	1·16
				24·5	1·22	1·93

1 MN/m≡2·549 ton/in

discrepancy will become more significant as the separation is reduced. A value of H_m of 10^{-5} corresponds to a minimum film thickness of about 0·2 μm (7 μin.) in the experiment, while the quoted surface roughness of the disks is 0·1 μm (r.m.s.). The error between theory and experiment becomes appreciable at values of H less than 10^{-5}.

Crook's results are summarized in Chapter 9. The film shape measured in the beautiful experiment described there looks very like the sort of shape predicted in the theory, and nothing need be added here to the discussion of this result in Chapter 9. About the vast range of film thickness measurements it may be noted that the variation with load was so small (*less than* indicated by the theory) that, within ± 15 per cent, all the results, regardless of variations of load or of the degree of sliding, could be expressed by the formula (9.7)

$$h = 2 \cdot 5 \ (u \eta_s)^{0 \cdot 5} \qquad\qquad (9.7)$$

where h is in microns and $u \eta_s$ is in N/m. The geometric mean of the range of values of $u \eta_s$ explored is about $0 \cdot 1$ N/m, so at this value the film thickness is $0 \cdot 8$ μm. To compare this with the theory we must set down the values of the experimental variables:

$$w = 1 \cdot 2 \times 10^5 \ \text{N/m}$$

$$\eta_0 u = u \eta_s = 0 \cdot 1 \ \text{N/m}$$

$$R = 19 \cdot 8 \ \text{mm}$$

$$E' = 2 \cdot 3 \times 10^{11} \ \text{N/m}^2$$

So

$$W = \frac{w}{E'R} = 2 \cdot 64 \times 10^{-5}$$

$$U = \frac{\eta_0 u}{E'R} = 2 \cdot 2 \times 10^{-11}$$

The value of G for steel and a mineral oil will be about 5000. The theoretical formula (7.1) gives for the minimum film thickness $0 \cdot 72$ μm; at this load the centre-line film thickness will be about 15 per cent bigger than the minimum, so the theoretical value is $0 \cdot 82$ μm, compared with the measured $0 \cdot 8$ μm. These agree therefore within experimental error. However, over the whole speed range, a discrepancy is evident because the experimental results show

$$h \propto (u \eta_s)^{0 \cdot 5}$$

while the theory predicts

$$h \propto (u \eta_s)^{0 \cdot 7}$$

So although in the middle of the speed range the agreement is good, the discrepancy which would arise one order of magnitude at each side can be seen in the ratios below:

$$u\eta_s \propto 0{\cdot}1 \quad 1 \quad 10$$

$$h \text{ experimental} \propto 0{\cdot}32 \quad 1 \quad 3{\cdot}2$$

$$h \text{ theoretical} \propto 0{\cdot}2 \quad 1 \quad 5$$

This error is significant, but the theory gives a close indication of the film thickness as Fig. 11.3 shows. This figure is a reproduction of Fig. 9.11 (a) with the theoretical line added. Crook

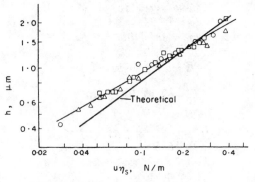

Fig. 11.3. Comparison of theory and Crook's experiments.

(1961a) examined the possibility of the source of the discrepancy being in his experiments, but he found no errors of the required magnitude. A possible explanation, in terms of non-Newtonian behaviour of the fluid, is given in Chapter 10. An important feature of Crook's results is that the film thickness, expressed in terms of $u\eta_s$, is surprisingly insensitive to quite severe degrees of sliding.

Two papers published when this monograph was in press describe film thickness measurements in disk machines which significantly increase the volume of experimental data. In a paper devoted chiefly to the effects of pressure and temperature on some physical properties of lubricants, Galvin, Naylor and Wilson (1964) present, almost as an aside, a large number of film thicknesses measured by the disk capacitance method; their derived measurements are based on values of the physical properties of the lubricant prevailing in the contact zone. They display their results graphically in the form of a comparison with values calculated according to the theoretical formula (7.1); the agreement is almost perfect. No details are given in the paper about the values of load and speed in the experiments, but the film thickness measurements cover a range of a little over one order of magnitude. In the other paper Christensen (1964b) presents in detail film thickness measurements over a wide range of loads and speeds. The rate of oil flow through the contact was determined by measuring the displacement relative to the machine frame of a lightly loaded pad riding on the surface film ahead of the contact; this displacement was measured with a variable inductance pickup. Christensen found that this results could be expressed in the form

$$ h = \frac{k(u\eta_s)^{0 \cdot 83}}{w^{0 \cdot 2}} $$

Although the variations of h with w and $u\eta_s$ are in reasonably close agreement with the theory, it will be seen that both are slightly bigger than the theory suggests.

The overall agreement between theory and experiment is better than could reasonably have been expected when the simplifying assumptions in the theory were made. There remain, however, the slight differences between the principal sets of published experimental results, particularly with respect to the variation of film thickness with the parameter $(\eta_0 u)$. Nonetheless, the foregoing comparisons show that the theoretical formula (7.1) can be used with some confidence to calculate the film thickness in a practical lubricated contact, provided that a reasonable estimate of the bulk solid temperature can be made.

A final small point on Crook's results concerns the friction force. Figure 10.8 shows the friction force in pure rolling. A value of F_R of 100 N/m occurs at a $u\eta_s$ of about 0·16 N/m. It can be deducted from Fig. 7.14 that the theoretical value is 130 N/m. The latter value is of course based on an iso-thermal calculation and lends support to Crook's conclusion that the temperature variation in the lubricant in pure rolling is small, even in the high pressure zone.

A Simplified Formula for Film Thickness

The vast majority of machine element contacts are between metal and metal with a film of mineral oil acting as lubricant. For these conditions, and taking account of the experimental results, the formula for film thickness can be reduced, to a fair approximation, to a simple slide-rule calculation. Written in dimensional terms the formula is (7.2)

$$h = \frac{1·6\alpha^{0·6}(\eta_0 u)^{0·7}(E')^{0·03}R^{0·43}}{w^{0·13}}$$

The effects of E' and w are small enough to be neglected in this context. Also the variation of α amongst conventional lubricants is not great, so $\alpha^{0·6}$ will not be influential. We can write there-fore, to a good approximation

$$h \propto (\eta_0 u)^{0·7} R^{0·43}$$

According to Crook's experiments

$$h \propto (\eta_0 u)^{0·5}$$

and in the spirit of this simplification

$$R^{0·43} \approx R^{0·5}$$

so we ought not to be far out with

$$h = k(\eta_0 u R)^{1/2}$$

In S.I. units the constant k is $1\cdot6 \times 10^{-5}$. Thus with η_0 in Pas, u in m/s and R in m,

$$h = 16 \, (\eta_0 u R)^{1/2} \, \mu\text{m}. \tag{11.1}$$

[With η_0 in poise, u in inches per second and R in inches

$$h = 5 \, (\eta_0 u R)^{1/2} \, \mu\text{in}.]$$

η_0 is the viscosity of the lubricant at the conditions of entry to the contact zone (the "controlling viscosity"), viz. at the surface temperature of the solids at entry, and normally at atmospheric pressure. u is the mean of the surface velocities of the solids, $\frac{1}{2}(u_1 + u_2)$, and R is the effective radius of the two cylindrical surfaces in contact, $(1/R) = (1/R_1) + (1/R_2)$.

In general, viscosity varies sharply with temperature, and the estimation of the bulk temperature of the solids in contact will be the most speculative feature of the calculation. Within this limitation the simple formula (11.1) will give the designer a good idea of the film thickness to be expected between *perfectly smooth surfaces.* The relation of this to the height of the irregularities on the actual surfaces will determine the efficacy of the hydro-dynamic lubrication.

In conclusion, a few remarks should be made about some physical effects of possible importance which have not so far been fully incorporated in the theory, primarily thermal effects. Crook's experiments and theory show that film thickness is little influenced by thermal effects; that the magnitude of lubricant flow through the pressure zone is determined in the inlet sweep, where the viscous heat generation is small in rolling or sliding, and the fluid, once in at the front has to come out at the back, so its volume, and therefore its thickness, is not much affected by heating in the zone. The main effects of temperature rise in the fluid will be on the friction force and the pressure distribution on the outlet side. The effect on friction has been amply demonstrated earlier. As far as the outlet pressure curve is concerned, there are considerations other than thermal which might modify the pressure peak. With a substantial degree of sliding between the surfaces the rise in temperature would sufficiently reduce the viscosity to have some effect on the pressure peak. But even in pure rolling it is probable that the pressure curve will be modified by non-Newtonian characteristics of the fluid. A full analysis must take account of thermal effects and the non-Newtonian rheological properties of the lubricant. It will be a formidable task.

CHAPTER 12

ANALYSIS OF ROLLER BEARINGS

IN EARLIER chapters the subject of elasto-hydrodynamic lubrication has been developed in relation to idealized contacts between two cylinders or between an equivalent cylinder and a plane. We now turn to the analysis of a real machine component which relies upon nominal rolling contact for its success; the roller bearing. The calculation of minimum oil film thickness in a typical roller bearing has been considered in Chapters 4 and 7, and attention will now be focused on other features of theoretical roller bearing performance. It should however be noted that whereas theoretical film thickness predictions in equivalent contacts have been well and truly confirmed by experiment over a wide range of operating conditions, no conclusive experimental support is yet available for the theoretical predictions of roller and cage motions and bearing deflections now to be presented. The results should be accepted as a demonstration of the application of conventional and elasto-hydrodynamic theory to real contacts and the limitations created by the assumptions clearly appreciated. The experimental information currently available suggests that much of the analysis is along the right lines, and within the restrictions referred to above it is hoped that it will form a backcloth for subsequent experimental investigations.

In the analysis of roller and cage kinematics three distinct contact conditions will be considered. These conditions will represent dry contact; rigid components lubricated by an isoviscous fluid; and elastic components lubricated by a fluid exhibiting a pressure dependent viscosity. For the lubricated contacts the first conditions represent a conventional hydrodynamic analysis whilst the second conditions are typical of an elastohydrodynamic analysis.

Roller Bearing kinematics for Dry Contact

A typical roller in a roller bearing assembly is shown in Fig. 12.1(a). The velocities relative to rotating axes $XO'Y$ are shown in Fig. 12.1(b). For convenience the angular velocity of a roller centre about the bearing centre (ω_c) is referred to fixed axes whilst the angular velocity of a roller about its own centre (ω) is referred to the rotating axes $XO'Y$. The angular velocity of the roller relative to the fixed coordinate system is given by the difference between ω_c and ω.

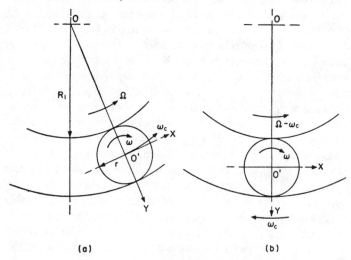

(a)   (b)

Fig. 12.1. (ω = angular velocity of roller relative to rotating axes $XO'Y$).
Coordinate system and angular velocities — dry contact.

[Reproduced by kind permission from the *Proceedings of the Institution of Mechanical Engineers Lubrication and Wear Convention* (1963).]

In pure rolling the surface velocity of the roller must equal the surface velocity of the appropriate track. Hence,

$$r\omega = R_1(\Omega - \omega_c)$$

$$r\omega = (R_1 + 2r)\,\omega_c$$

These equations yield the following well-known expressions,

$$\omega_c = \frac{\Omega}{2(1 + s)} \qquad (12.1)$$

$$\omega = \frac{(1 + 2s)}{2s(1 + s)}\,\Omega \qquad (12.2)$$

where

$$s = \frac{r}{R_1}$$

Lubrication Analysis for a Constant Viscosity Lubricant and Rigid Bearing Components

In a lubricated roller bearing the two main problems which emerge are the calculation of minimum oil film thickness between the rollers and the inner and outer tracks and the determination of the motion of the roller.

Roller Dynamics

The characteristics of the lubricant films between a roller and the inner and outer tracks can be established from the equivalent cylinder concept presented in Chapter 1. The force components and surface velocities for a typical roller are shown in Fig. 12.2; the suffices i and o being used to refer to the oil films between the roller and the *inner* and *outer* tracks respectively.

For steady state motion the equilibrium equations for the roller are,

$$X \qquad\qquad P_{xi} + F_i = P_{xo} + F_o \qquad\qquad (12.3)$$

$$Y \qquad\qquad P_{yo} - P_{yi} = m(r + R_1)\,\omega_c^2 \qquad\qquad (12.4)$$

$$\text{Moments} \qquad\qquad F_i + F_o = 0 \qquad\qquad (12.5)$$

The term on the right-hand side of eqn. (12.4) represents the inertia loading on the roller due to its rotation about the bearing centre.

Expressions for the six force components per unit length of cylinder can be written down directly from eqns. (3.15).

$$\left. \begin{aligned}
P_{xi} &= \frac{2}{(1+s)}\, 4{\cdot}5\eta u_i \left[\left(\frac{R}{h_0}\right)_i\right]^{1/2} \\[2ex]
P_{xo} &= \frac{2(1+2s)}{(1+s)}\, 4{\cdot}5\eta u_0 \left[\left(\frac{R}{h_0}\right)_0\right]^{1/2} \\[2ex]
P_{yi} &= 2 \times 2{\cdot}45\eta u_i \left(\frac{R}{h_0}\right)_i \\[2ex]
P_{yo} &= 2 \times 2{\cdot}45\eta u_0 \left(\frac{R}{h_0}\right)_0 \\[2ex]
F_i &= -4{\cdot}5\eta u_i \left[\left(\frac{R}{h_0}\right)_i\right]^{1/2} + 3{\cdot}48\eta v_i \left[\left(\frac{R}{h_0}\right)_i\right]^{1/2} \\[2ex]
F_o &= -4{\cdot}5\eta u_0 \left[\left(\frac{R}{h_0}\right)_0\right]^{1/2} + 3{\cdot}48\eta v_0 \left[\left(\frac{R}{h_0}\right)_0\right]^{1/2}
\end{aligned} \right\} \qquad (12.6)$$

The friction force expressions in eqns. (12.6) include the maximum contribution from the cavitated zone compatible with the cavitation boundary condition discussed in Chapter 3. The terms

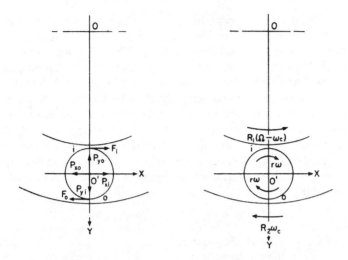

(a) hydrodynamic forces   (b) surface velocities

FIG. 12.2. Force components and surface velocities —lubricated contact.

[Reproduced by kind permission from the *Proceedings of the Institution of Mechanical Engineers Lubrication and Wear Convention* (1963).]

u and v in eqn. (12.6) respectively denote the mean and the difference of the surface velocities.

$$u_{i,o} = \left(\frac{u_1 + u_2}{2} \right)_{i,o}$$

$$v_{i,o} = (u_1 - u_2)_{i,o}$$

A full statement of the expressions for u and v is given in Table 12.1.

TABLE 12.1. SURFACE VELOCITIES

	Contact i	Contact o
$2u = (u_1 + u_2)$	$2u_i = R_1(\Omega - \omega_c) + r\omega$	$2u_o = (R_1 + 2r)\,\omega_c + r\omega$
$v = (u_1 - u_2)$	$v_1 = R_1(\Omega - \omega_c) - r\omega$	$v_0 = (R_1 + 2r)\,\omega_c - r\omega$

When the force components (12.6) and the velocity expressions given in Table 12.1 are introduced into the equilibrium equations, four unknowns become evident. The unknowns are normally the rotational velocities ω and ω_c and the minimum film thicknesses (h_0) at contacts i and o. It will be seen that the rotational velocities can be uniquely determined from the equilibrium equations, and in the absence of centrifugal effects the ratio of the minimum film thickness will also emerge. The actual values of the minimum oil film thickness will be determined if the load on each roller is known. Alternatively for a rigid bearing geometry with known radial clearance the following relationship will enable the film thicknesses to be calculated.

$$(h_0)_i + (h_0)_o = \Delta\,(1 - n\cos\theta)$$

where $\Delta =$ the radial clearance

$\quad\;\; n =$ the eccentricity ratio

$\quad\;\; \theta =$ an angle measured from the load line

With $(h_0)_i$ and $(h_0)_o$ determined the load carried by each roller can be computed.

The angular velocities ω and ω_c can be expressed as fractions of the epicyclic values given by eqns. (12.1) and (12.2) as follows:

$$\alpha = \frac{\omega_c}{\Omega}\,2(1 + s) \qquad\qquad (12.7)$$

$$\beta = \frac{\omega}{\Omega}\,\frac{2s(1 + s)}{(1 + 2s)} \qquad\qquad (12.8)$$

The values of α and β are functions of s only, and values have been computed by solving numerically the equilibrium equations for values of s ranging from 0 to 0·5. In these solutions centrifugal effects have been neglected. For very light loads and high speeds it will be necessary to include centrifugal forces in the analysis. For a 16 mm diameter steel roller running on an inner track of diameter 64 mm the centrifugal force corresponding to a shaft speed of 5000 rev/min is approximately 17·26 kN/m (15·8 lbf/in).

The calculated values of α and β are plotted against s in Fig. 12.3. The two notable features of Fig. 12.3 are the low values of β at all values of s and the steady decrease in α with increasing s. The latter result indicates that cage slip can be expected in a lightly loaded bearing of conventional proportions. The rollers rotate about the bearing centre with epicyclic velocity given by

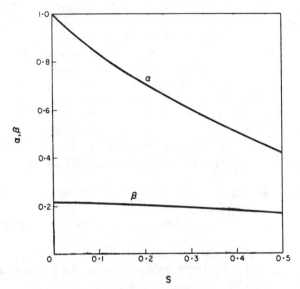

FIG. 12.3. Effect of curvature on roller motion.
[Reproduced by kind permission from the *Proceedings of the Institution of Mechanical Engineers Lubrication and Wear Convention* (1963).]

eqn. (12.1) only when the roller radius is insignificant compared with the radius of the inner track ($s \to 0$). In this condition it is clear that $F_i = F_o = 0$, but for all values of s other than zero $F_i = -F_o \neq 0$.

The present calculation yields a limiting value of β of 0·215, whereas Osterle (1959) calculates a value of 0·107. This difference arises because the present analysis includes the maximum permissible shear force from the cavitated region whilst Osterle's analysis ignores the effect. For this reason the above values represent upper and lower bounds to the values of β for $s = 0$. It is interesting to note that the inclusion of shear forces in the cavitated zone doubles the rate of rotation of a roller about its own axis. This demonstrates how very small torques may greatly affect the rotation of the rollers, and since extraneous torque from the cage has been omitted from the analysis too much importance should not be attached to the numerical values of β. In spite of this observation the very low values of β do suggest that considerable slip can be expected between the rollers and the races of a lightly loaded bearing.

The above theoretical conclusions are not inconsistent with C. F. Smith's (1962) experimental results. For a lightly loaded roller bearing having an s value of approximately 0·08, Smith records a steady state cage slip at 12,000 rev/min of about 20 per cent. The theoretical value as determined from Fig. 12.3 is 12 per cent.

The previous discussion is based upon the assumption that an oil film can be established between the rolling elements. This assumption can be tested by referring to the roller bearing example presented in Chapter 4. In the example it was found that the predicted film thickness was small compared with the surface roughness of typical bearing components. It appears that effective lubricating films can only be expected at very light loads or high speeds, and the rigid component analysis presented in this section must be restricted to these conditions. It should also be recalled that centrifugal forces, which are likely to be of maximum significance at low loads and high speeds, have not been included in the numerical analysis.

One of the main objects of the present Chapter is to apply the new results of elasto-hydrodynamic theory to roller bearing contacts and to compare the results of the investigation with the rigid component analysis. Apart from an examination of the effects of local elastic deformation on the lubrication of roller bearing contacts it is appropriate to consider the deformation of a complete bearing assembly.

Elastic Deformation of a Roller Bearing Assembly

The deformation of a single roller and its supporting races, neglecting any dynamic effect, has been examined in detail by Dowson and Higginson (1963). In that paper it is shown that deflection is proportional to $(\text{load})^{0 \cdot 9}$, and that a linear relation gives a good working approximation. This section is devoted to a general examination of the deformation of a complete roller bearing assembly.

Distribution of Load on Rollers

Consider a complete roller bearing assembly.

Let

W' = total load unit length of rollers.

P_0' = maximum load carried by the most heavily loaded roller.

Z = total number of rollers.

$M = W'/P_0'$ = load distribution factor.

Stribeck calculated the distribution of load in a geometrically perfect ball bearing (see for instance, Allan), where the deflection of each element is proportional to $(\text{load})^{2/3}$. He found that while M increased with the number of balls Z, the ratio Z/M remained just about constant at a value near $4 \cdot 37$. It will be shown later that, if we assume for a roller that deflection is proportional to load (rather than $(\text{load})^{0 \cdot 9}$) then Z/M is constant at 4 for bearings with even numbers of rollers, and very close to 4 for odd numbers. Now $0 \cdot 9$ is nearer to 1 than to 2/3, so it seems quite reasonable to accept the figure 4 for perfect geometry and, in analysing the deflection of the whole bearing, to assume that the displacement of each roller element is linear.

If we assume that the bearing assembly and all its components are geometrically perfect then, after Stribeck, we see from Fig. 12.4 that for small deflections

$$\delta_1 = \delta_0 \cos \lambda$$
$$\delta_2 = \delta_0 \cos 2\lambda \quad \text{etc.}$$

with

$$\lambda = \frac{360°}{Z}$$

$$W' = P_0' + 2P_1' \cos \lambda + \cdots + 2P_n' \cos n\lambda$$

up to a value of n equal to the integral part of $(Z - 1)/4$

$$P_0' = k\delta_0$$

$$P_1' = k\delta_1 \quad \text{etc.}$$

$$\frac{W'}{P_0'} = 1 + 2\cos^2\lambda + \cdots + 2\cos^2 n\lambda$$

Values of the right-hand side are shown in Table 12.2.

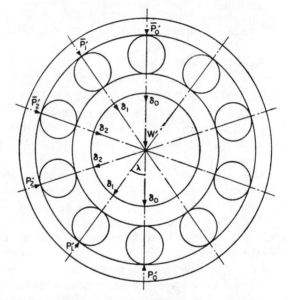

FIG. 12.4. Forces (P') and radial components of displacement (δ) in a roller bearing.

[Reproduced by kind permission from the *Proceedings of the Institution of Mechanical Engineers Lubrication and Wear Convention* (1963).]

TABLE 12.2

Z	4	5	6	7	8	9	10	12	15	20
M	1	1·9096	1·5	1·7775	2	2·2339	2·5	3·0	3·7556	5·0
Z/M	4	4·198	4	3·938	4	4·029	4	4	3·994	4

Table 12.2 shows that in a geometrically perfect bearing the most heavily loaded roller carries a load approximately equal to $4W'/Z$.

Bearing Stiffness: Effects of Geometrical Imperfections

It has been shown elsewhere (Dowson and Higginson, 1963) that the total deflection of a single roller and its races in a realistic bearing arrangement is given to a high degree of accuracy by the expression,

$$\frac{\delta}{r} = 7 \cdot 2 \left(\frac{P'K}{r} \right)^{0 \cdot 9}$$

where δ = deflection

P' = load/unit length

r = roller radius

K = an elastic constant equal to $2(1 - \sigma^2)/\pi E$ (the relation between the constants K and E' is $K = 2/\pi E'$).

A good working approximation to the previous expression is the linear relation,

$$\frac{\delta}{r} = 17 \cdot 5 \left(\frac{P'K}{r} \right)$$

The expression can, of course, be written,

$$\delta = 17 \cdot 5 P'K$$

which indicates that, within the approximations involved, the deflection is independent of the roller radius. The deflection of a complete and geometrically perfect bearing will be given by P'_0, the load per unit length on the most heavily loaded roller, which is $4W''/Z$.

$$\delta = \frac{70KW'}{Z}$$

EXAMPLE. Consider a roller bearing for a 50 mm (1·97 in.) shaft with 10 rollers. Maximum Hertzian pressure = 1544 MPa (100 tons/in²). Length of roller = 16 mm (0·63 in.). Total load on bearing = 17·8kN (4000 lb.) Deflection at maximum load = 22 μm (0·9 × 10⁻³ in.).

We next examine the effect on the stiffness of geometrical imperfections in the assembly; in particular the cases of initial radial clearance and interference, assuming that the geometry is otherwise perfect: i.e. the rollers are identical and cylindrical, and the races are circular. Now a roller can sustain compression but not, of course, tension, so in the spirit of Macaulay we write an expression for the load carried by a single roller in terms of the deflection in the form

$$P' = k\{x\}$$

where

$$\{x\} = x \quad \text{when} \quad x \geq 0$$

$$\{x\} = 0 \quad \text{when} \quad x < 0$$

and k is the stiffness of a single roller and its races.

Consider first a bearing with a small initial radial clearance, Δ. Referring again to Fig. 12.4 it is plain that no load is carried by rollers 0, 1, 2, etc., until the displacement of the shaft from the centre is such that δ_0, δ_1, δ_2, etc., in turn exceed Δ. The load is first carried by roller 0 alone, but as the load, and therefore the deflection, increases, the other rollers in turn come into contact and help to carry the load. As before

$$\frac{W'}{P_0'} = 1 + 2\frac{P_1'}{P_0'}\cos\lambda + 2\frac{P_2'}{P_0'}\cos 2\lambda + \text{etc.}$$

but now

$$P_0' = k\{\delta_0 - \Delta\}$$

$$P_1' = k\{\delta_1 - \Delta\}$$

With any load at all, $\delta_0 > \Delta$, so the same procedure as above leads to

$$\frac{W'}{P_0'} = 1 + \frac{2}{\delta_0 - \Delta} \times$$

$$\times \, [\{\delta_0 \cos \lambda - \Delta\} \cos \lambda + \cdots + \{\delta_0 \cos n\lambda - \Delta\} \cos n\lambda]$$

Next consider a bearing which is assembled with a radial interference ε. If the bearing is mounted on a shaft and in a housing which are rigid enough to keep the races circular, then there will be initially a force transmitted by each roller equal to $k\varepsilon$. Under an external load W', the shaft will deflect δ_0 and, as before,

$$\delta_1 = \delta_0 \cos \lambda \quad \text{etc.}$$

The force transmitted by a roller will now be

$$P_0' = k\{\varepsilon + \delta_0\}$$

$$P_1' = k\{\varepsilon + \delta_1\} \quad \text{etc.}$$

and

$$\overline{P}_0' = k\{\varepsilon - \delta_0\}$$

$$\overline{P}_1' = k\{\varepsilon - \delta_1\}$$

The notation is self-evident in Fig. 12.4. Proceeding as before, and remembering that throughout this section the brackets { } have the significance assigned to them earlier, we obtain

$$\frac{W'}{P_0'} = 1 + \frac{2}{\{\varepsilon + \delta_0\}} \times$$

$$\times \, [\{\varepsilon + \delta_0 \cos \lambda\} \cos \lambda + \{\varepsilon + \delta_0 \cos 2\lambda\} \cos 2\lambda + \text{etc.}]$$

$$- \frac{\{\varepsilon - \delta_0\}}{\{\varepsilon + \delta_0\}} - \frac{2}{\{\varepsilon + \delta_0\}} \times$$

$$\times \, [\{\varepsilon - \delta_0 \cos \lambda\} \cos \lambda + \{\varepsilon - \delta_0 \cos 2\lambda\} \cos 2\lambda + \text{etc.}]$$

As an example, the deflection (given directly by P_0') of a 10-roller bearing has been calculated from these expressions for three conditions (*a*) perfect geometry, (*b*) an initial radial clearance of $10^{-3} \times$ (the roller radius) and (*c*) an initial radial interference of the same magnitude. The results are shown in dimensionless terms in Fig. 12.5. For the bearing described in the

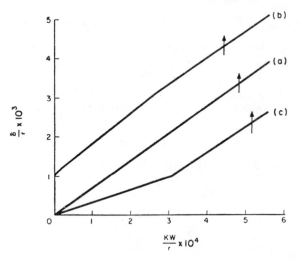

FIG. 12.5. Stiffness of roller bearing assembly. (a) Perfect geometry. (b) Initial radial clearance $\varDelta/r = 1 \times 10^{-3}$. (c) Initial Radial Interference $\varepsilon/r = 1 \times 10^{-3}$. ↑ indicates maximum Hertzian stress = 1544 MPa (100 t.s.i.)

[Reproduced by kind permission from the *Proceedings of the Institution of Mechanical Engineers Lubrication and Wear Convention* (1963).]

earlier example for a 50 mm (1·97 in.) shaft this quantity represents a clearance or interference as small as 8×10^{-3} mm (0.3×10^{-3} in.).

With the clearance the result is just as would be expected – the stiffness only slightly affected apart from the initial displacement due to the clearance itself, the most heavily loaded roller carrying rather more than its fair share of load, and the maximum permissible load thereby slightly reduced. The maximum permissible load is arbitrarily fixed at a value of KW'/r corresponding to a maximum Hertzian pressure of 1544 M Pa (100 tons/in²) in a steel contact.

The effect of a small interference is more interesting. The stiffness is markedly increased—doubled while all the rollers are in compression—and, surprisingly, the maximum permissible load is slightly increased. This last effect arises only when the interference is small; plainly a large enough interference will engender a force in the rollers which alone exceeds the maximum permissible. The explanation of this increase is this; the maximum load is determined by the compression of the most heavily loaded roller, in the present example a deflection of the roller element given by $\delta/r = 3\cdot5 \times 10^{-3}$: with 1×10^{-3} clearance the total deflection is $4\cdot5 \times 10^{-3}$ at maximum load; with 1×10^{-3} interference it is $2\cdot5 \times 10^{-3}$ which, by virtue of the increased stiffness, corresponds to a slightly higher maximum load.

A film of lubricant constitutes a small radial interference in a bearing which is initially perfect, but the next section will show that it is a good deal smaller than the interference in Fig. 12.5.

Elasto-hydrodynamic Force Components

The question of load sharing between the rollers has been examined in some detail in the previous section and we now return to the question of lubrication. The relationship between minimum film thickness and normal force components in an elasto-hydrodynamic contact is now well established. In order to solve the equilibrium equation it is also necessary to have expressions for the tangential pressure and friction force components.

Tangential Pressure Force Components for a Cylinder Near a Plane

In general the diminsionless pressure force component acting on the cylinder $P'_x (= P_x/E'R)$ will be a function of the dimensionless material (G), velocity (U) and normal force (W) parameters encountered in elasto-hydrodynamic theory (see Chapter 6).

$$P'_x = \varphi(G, U, W)$$

(P'_x is employed to distinguish this dimensionless representation for P_x from the one employed in Chapter 3) where

$$G = \alpha E', \quad U = \frac{\eta_0 u}{E'R} \quad \text{and} \quad W = \frac{w}{E'R}$$

It has been noted by Dowson, Higginson and Whitaker (1962) that P'_x is almost independent of W, and for a particular combination of elastic solids (E') and lubricant (α); P'_x simply becomes a function of U.

$$P'_x = \varphi(U)$$

Values of P_x have been computed for the five values of U considered in Chapter 7 and the results are shown in Table 12.3.

TABLE 12.3

U	10^{-13}	10^{-12}	10^{-11}	10^{-10}	10^{-9}
P'_x	6.4×10^{-10}	4.2×10^{-9}	2.4×10^{-8}	1.11×10^{-7}	4.2×10^{-7}

A log–log plot of these results in non-linear and hence a simple relationship is bound to be inadequate. It is found that an equation of the following form reproduces P'_x at values of U of 10^{-12} and 10^{-10}.

$$P'_x = 1.43 U^{0.71} \tag{12.9}$$

The power of U can vary considerably if expressions designed to reproduce P'_x at other values of U are obtained. The power of U in eqn. (12.9) is very close to the value of 0·7 which occurs in the film thickness eqn. (7.1), and in subsequent calculations it will be equated to 0·7. It should also be emphasized that eqn. (12.9) s related to a value of G of 5000.

Friction Force Components for a Cylinder Near a Plane

In dimensionless terms the viscous surface force acting on the cylinder in a contact can be written as.

$$F' = \frac{F}{E'R} = -\frac{P'_x}{2} + \frac{(u_1 - u_2)}{E'R} \int \frac{\eta}{h} \, dx \ldots \tag{12.10}$$

(Again the symbol F' is used to distinguish this dimensionless form of F from the group employed for rigid cylinders in Chapter 3.)

The first term on the right-hand side represents the friction force in pure rolling, and the second term is the contribution due to sliding. Before the integral in the equation can be evaluated the relationship between η (and hence p), and x must be established. The following exponential viscosity–pressure relationship will be used,

$$\eta = \eta_0\, e^{\alpha p} \quad (= \eta_0\, e^{GP})$$

By making this assumption we are neglecting thermal effects in the contact. Crook's experiments described in Chapter 10 clearly demonstrated that this is valid only if the sliding velocities are very small. We shall see that the analysis does in fact predict a negligible degree of sliding.

The spectacular effect of pressure on viscosity ensures that most of the sliding friction arises in the high pressure zone of a lubricated contact. It has been shown earlier that under high loads and realistic speeds the pressure distribution approximates to the Hertzian ellipse of dry contact, and that the film thickness is effectively constant throughout most of the Hertzian zone. An elliptical pressure distribution and a film thickness independent of x will therefore be assumed. In these circumstances eqn. (12.10) becomes,

$$F' = -\frac{P'_x}{2} + V\left(\frac{R}{h}\right) I$$

where

$$V = \frac{\eta_0(u_1 - u_2)}{E'R}, \quad I = \int_{-b/R}^{b/R} e^{\,GP_0\left[1 - \left(\frac{R\bar{x}}{b}\right)^2\right]^{1/2}} d\bar{x}$$

and

$$\bar{x} = \frac{x}{R}$$

$P_0 = \left(\dfrac{W}{2\pi}\right)^{1/2}$ — Hertzian maximum pressure in dimensionless

form $\left(\dfrac{p_0}{E'}\right)$ b (Hertzian half-zone width) $= 4P_0R$

210   ANALYSIS OF ROLLER BEARINGS

Roller Bearing Lubrication Analysis for Pressure Dependent Viscosity and Elastic Bearing Components

In dimensionless form the equilibrium equations become,

$$P'_{xi} + F'_i = \frac{(R)_o}{(R)_i}(P'_{x0} + F'_0)$$

$$\frac{(R)_o}{(R)_i} W_o - W_i = \frac{m}{E'}\left(\frac{(R)_i + r}{(R)_i}\right)\omega_c^2$$

$$F'_i + \frac{(R)_o}{(R)_i} F'_0 = 0$$

Where (R) denotes the radius of curvature of the equivalent cylinder near a plane. The force components P'_x and F' for contacts i and o are,

$$P'_{xi} = \frac{1}{(1+s)} 1\cdot 43 U_i^{0\cdot 7}$$

$$P'_{xo} = \frac{(1+2s)}{(1+s)} 1\cdot 43 U_o^{0\cdot 7}$$

$$F'_i = -0\cdot 715 U_i^{0\cdot 7} + V_i\left(\frac{R}{h}\right)_i I_i$$

$$F'_o = -0\cdot 715 U_o^{0\cdot 7} + V_o\left(\frac{R}{h}\right)_o I_o$$

Also the relationship between film thickness and W is obtained directly from eqn. (7.1).

$$\left(\frac{h}{R}\right)_i = \frac{1\cdot 6 G^{0\cdot 6} U_i^{0\cdot 7}}{W_i^{0\cdot 13}} = \frac{265 U_i^{0\cdot 7}}{W_i^{0\cdot 13}}$$

$$\left(\frac{h}{R}\right)_o = \frac{1\cdot 6 G^{0\cdot 6} U_o^{0\cdot 7}}{W_o^{0\cdot 13}} = \frac{265 U_o^{0\cdot 7}}{W_o^{0\cdot 13}}$$

Again it should be emphasized that the above force expressions are based on a value of G of 5000. This value is representative of steel rollers lubricated with a mineral oil.

Solutions of the equilibrium equations and the force component equations have to be related to specific loads, speeds and material properties. In this sense solutions for an elasto-hydrodynamic contact differ from the rigid component solutions, where it was found that α and β were independent of speed and load. The numerical work involved in obtaining solutions to the equilibrium equations for an elasto-hydrodynamic contact is considerably greater than the work involved in the analysis of a rigid contact. The results presented below were obtained on a digital computer. Solutions for α and β as defined by eqns. (12.7) and (12.8) have been obtained for the following cases for values of s ranging from 0 to 0·5.

Case 1	Case 2
$R_1 = 33\cdot338$ mm $(1\cdot3125$ in.$)$	$R_1 = 33\cdot338$ mm $(1\cdot3125$ in.$)$
$\Omega = 500$ rad/s	$\Omega = 500$ rad/s
$E' = 228$ GPa $(33 \times 10^6 \text{lb/in}^2)$	$E' = 228$ GPa $(33 \times 10^6 \text{lb/in}^2)$
$\eta_0 = 0\cdot05$ Pas	$\eta_0 = 0\cdot01$ Pas
$W = 4\cdot7 \times 10^{-5}$	$W = 2\cdot15 \times 10^{-4}$
$G = 5000$	$G = 5000$

It should be noted that for a fixed value of W the load per unit length of roller diminishes as s decreases. On the scale to which Fig. 12.3 is plotted neither α nor β for an elasto-hydrodynamic contact can be distinguished from unity. The computer values are therefore presented in Table 12.4.

It is immediately apparent from Table 12.4 that the motion of the rollers as determined by elasto-hydrodynamic analysis is essentially epicyclic. This result arises primarily from the very considerable increase in viscosity experienced by the lubricant in the contact. For an exceptionally viscous fluid a minute slip, or sliding motion, will transmit the shear forces encountered in a roller bearing.

TABLE 12.4

s	0	0·1	0·2	0·3	0·4	0·5
Case 1	1·00000	1·00001	1·00003	1·00005	1·00007	1·00008
	1·00000	0·99997	0·99996	0·99995	0·99994	0·99994
Case 2	1·00000	1·00000	1·00000	1·00000	1·00000	1·00000
	1·00000	1·00000	1·00000	1·00000	1·00000	1·00000

The influence of centrifugal action on the computed values of α and β is neglible because the additional forces are insignificant compared with the applied loads. It is inconceivable that the minute variations from epicyclic motion predicted by the theory for highly loaded contacts could be detected experimentally. However, the results indicate that a lack of measurable slip cannot be used to deny the existence of oil films in a roller bearing. Indeed, when elastic deformation and the effect of high pressure on viscosity is considered, the predicted oil film thickness is often significant when compared with the surface finish. For the example considered in the rigid component analysis, elasto-hydrodynamic theory predicts a maximum film thickness of $0·4$ μm (15 μin.). This figure promotes more confidence in the belief that the contact may operate hydrodynamically.

It is interesting to consider the magnitude of the force components acting on a typical roller. The values of F, P_x and P_y for Case 2 have been plotted against s in Fig. 12.6. In addition the minimum film thickness at each contact is recorded. In all cases the tangential pressure forces exceed the friction forces, and as the value of s approaches zero (small roller case) all the force components tend towards zero. The smallest film thickness occurs, as expected, at the contact between the roller and the inner race. Again it should be noted that the inner track radius is constant and the roller radius variable in the example. Different values of s could have been obtained by keeping the roller radius constant and varying the inner track radius. In the latter case the force components would differ from those shown in Fig. 12.6.

Finally it should be emphasized that the elasto-hydrodynamic analysis is, by virtue of some of the assumptions, a limiting case. It is known that the simple exponential viscosity–pressure

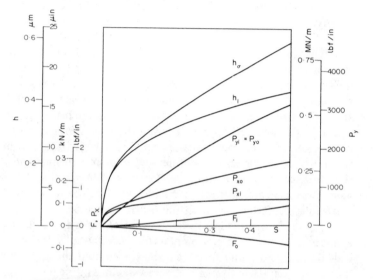

FIG. 12.6. Force components and minimum film thickness in a roller bearing — elasto-hydrodynamic analysis. $W = 21 \cdot 5 \times 10^{-5}$, $R_1 = 33 \cdot 338$ mm (1·3125 in.) $G = 5000$, $\eta_0 = 0 \cdot 01$ Pas.

[Reproduced by kind permission from the *Proceedings of the Institution of Mechanical Engineers Lubrication and Wear Convention* (1963).]

relationship is inadequate at high pressures, and although the predicted motion is very close to pure rolling thermal and non-Newtonian behaviour may also modify the numerical results. However, the values of α and β are so near to unity over a wide range of conditions that it would require a major effect to invalidate the above discussion. In practice the operating conditions of a bearing will fall between the rigid cylinder, constant viscosity situation and the elasto-hydrodynamic regime; the roller and cage motion to be expected being different in the two situations. The main conclusions to be drawn from this analysis of roller bearing lubrication and deformation are summarized below.

1. For a constant viscosity fluid and rigid bearing components the maximum angular velocity of a roller about its own centre is only about 20 per cent of the value expected in pure rolling. In addition the angular velocity of a roller about the bearing axis falls from 100 per cent to about 40 per cent of the epicyclic value as the ratio of the roller radius to the inner track radius increases from 0 to 0·5. These observations suggest that considerable roller slip and some cage slip can be expected in high speed, lightly loaded roller bearings of conventional proportions.

2. In a geometrically perfect bearing the most heavily loaded roller carries a load approximately equal to $4W'/Z$. Apart from the initial displacement the stiffness of a roller bearing is only slightly affected by a small radial clearance. The initial stiffness can however be considerably increased (doubled) by imposing a small initial interference upon the bearing assembly.

3. For a highly loaded roller bearing elasto-hydrodynamic analysis shows that the motion of a roller is essentially epicyclic. Calculations show that forces can be transmitted through film lubricated contacts between roller and tracks with neglible slip. Film thickness predictions confirm the possibility of a hydrodynamic contact mechanism in roller bearings. No detectable cage or roller slip can therefore be expected in highly loaded bearings. The actual motion of a roller in a given bearing will be located between the limiting cases computed for rigid and elastic components.

The application of conventional and elasto-hydrodynamic theory to the analysis of an ideal roller bearing has yielded results which differ considerably. In particular the effect of high pressure upon lubricant viscosity and local elastic deformation of the solids leads to a considerable improvement in the predicted film thickness and a major change in the theoretical roller motion.

When highly loaded lubricated contacts encountered in machinery are re-examined in the light of elasto-hydrodynamic theory it is frequently found that the film thickness has been underestimated by conventional theory. This observation is supported by the lubrication analysis of roller bearings. Furthermore, the change in the predicted motion of the rollers which becomes evident when high pressure effects are included in the analysis suggests that many experimental observations which have been in conflict with conventional lubrication analysis may yet find an explanation in elasto-hydrodynamic theory.

CHAPTER 13

A NOTE ON GEAR LUBRICATION

THE detailed mechanical action of gears, even of the simpler types, is very complicated; a full understanding of what happens at the contacts between the teeth has not yet been attained. Over a period of many years much experimental and theoretical work has been reported on all the aspects of gear functioning, including lubrication. Historically, the interest in the mechanism of gear lubrication was responsible for generating the field of activity which is the subject of this monograph.

In this last, short chapter we apply the results of earlier chapters to the simplest gear system — involute spur gears. Even in this system, the kinematic process is complicated; the gear teeth are continually coming in and out of mesh and the motion at any one contact involves a degree of sliding which changes in magnitude and sign in every cycle. So the steady state theory analyses a very imperfect model of the real thing, and its results must be applied with caution. (Similar remarks have often been made about disc machine experiments.)

It can be shown (see for example, Merritt, 1942) that the instantaneous local geometry and surface velocities at the contact between involute spur gear teeth at any point in the meshing cycle can be represented by the contact between two appropriate cylinders. These cylinders have radii equal to the local involute radii of curvature and rotate at the gear wheel speeds, as shown in Fig. 1.2. The approximate analogy is completed by loading the cylinders together under a load equal to the tooth load acting in the direction of the common tangent to the base circles. The film thicknesses to be calculated below are based on this steady-state two cylinder analogy; the contribution of any normal approach action arising from changes in the film thickness through the cycle is neglected.

It is clear that the radii of the equivalent cylinders vary through the meshing cycle, and the contact will also carry a varying load due to load sharing between successive pairs of teeth. The effect of these geometrical changes on film thickness will be examined in some detail, but the contact load will be assumed to be constant; this assumption will in itself do little to invalidate the analysis owing to the insignificant effect of load on film thickness. A representative film thickness for the meshing cycle is the pitch point value and this will be given for a wide range of operating conditions.

Referring now to Fig. 1.2, the centre distance of the gear wheels is

$$l = R_1 + R_2$$

The gear ratio (expressed here always as a number larger than 1) is

$$R_g = \frac{R_1}{R_2} = \frac{\Omega_2}{\Omega_1} = \frac{N_2}{N_1}$$

where N_1 and N_2 are the gear wheel speeds in rev/min. The calculations will be based on N_1, the speed of the larger wheel, as the standard speed.

$$R_1 = \frac{R_g l}{R_g + 1}, \quad R_2 = \frac{l}{R_g + 1}$$

The centre distance of the equivalent cylinders is constant and equal to $(R_1 + R_2) \sin \psi$, where ψ is the pressure angle of the gears. However, the radii of the cylinders vary according to the location of the tooth contact on the line of action, signified by s. So the equivalent radius of the pair of cylinders will be, at any instant,

$$R = \frac{(R_1 \sin \psi + s)(R_2 \sin \psi - s)}{(R_1 + R_2) \sin \psi}$$

The velocities through the contact region of the two surfaces are

$$u_1 = \frac{\pi N_1}{30} (R_1 \sin \psi + s)$$

$$u_2 = \frac{\pi N_2}{30} (R_2 \sin \psi - s)$$

The entraining velocity is $u = (u_1 + u_2)/2$ and so

$$u = \frac{\pi N_1}{30} \left[R_1 \sin \psi - \frac{s}{2} (R_g - 1) \right]$$

It will be noted that for $R_g = 1$, u is constant along the path of contact.

The film thickness can now be calculated for a contact at any distance s from the pitch point by the formula (7.1).

For involute gears the line of action coincides with the common tangent to the base circles, but the length of the path of contact depends essentially on the diametral pitch. The practical limits of the contact can be expressed geometrically in terms of the addenda of the wheel and pinion, A_1 and A_2 respectively. The path of contact covers the values of s from

$$- [\{(R_2 + A_2)^2 - R_2^2 \cos^2 \psi\}^{1/2} - R_2 \sin \psi]$$

to

$$+ [\{(R_1 + A_1)^2 - R_1^2 \cos^2 \psi\}^{1/2} - R_1 \sin \psi]$$

These limits are therefore determined entirely by the addenda.

All the results given below relate to steel gears lubricated by a mineral oil. The variation of film thickness throughout the cycle is shown in Fig. 13.1 for a centre distance of 0·3 m (12 in.), a gear ratio of 5, a wheel speed of 1000 r.p.m. and a tooth loading of 0·4 MN/m (1 ton/in.). For comparison the film thickness for rigid teeth and constant viscosity is also shown. Likely limits to the path of contact are shown on the curve for two values of the diametral pitch, 5 and 10 per in. (corresponding to values of the **module** of 0·2 and 0·1 in., or 5·08 and 2·54 mm). For each of these values, two sets of limits are shown. These correspond to two ways of calculating wheel and pinion addenda: (i) "Stand-

ard" addenda, i.e. equal addenda on wheel and pinion equal to
the inverse of the diametral pitch and (ii) Addenda calculated
according to B.S.S. 436 which gives British Standard tooth proportions. A feature of this diagram is its indication that, under
isothermal conditions, the thickest oil films for this gear ratio are
encountered during contact between the pinion tip and the wheel

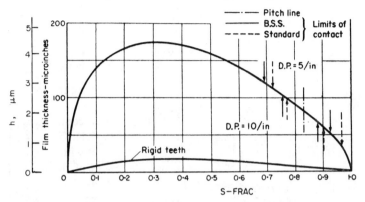

FIG. 13.1. Film thickness variation along line of action, showing
various limits of path of contact. Centre distance = 0·3 m
Load = 0·4 MN/m. Wheel speed = 1000 r.p.m. Gear ratio = 5.

flank, and that the thinnest films occur when the wheel tip is in
contact with the pinion flank. The earlier caution must be
emphasized about the reliability of the calculated values of
film thickness. At the pitch line, where the relative motion
of the teeth is pure rolling, the values of film thickness are
presented with some confidence, provided of course that
the bulk temperature of the metals is known closely enough
to permit a fair estimate of the viscosity to be made. At
points remote from the pitch point, the relative motion
contains a significant element of sliding, but disk machine
evidence suggests that this in itself will have little influence
on the film thickness, as long as the correct metal temperature is
applied to the calculation of viscosity. In practice, the factors
that may well invalidate the figures for film thickness near the
extremes of the path of contact are the inevitable geometrical

departures from perfect involutes, and the unsteady conditions at first contact.

Figure 13.2 shows the calculated variation of film thickness for a wide range of gear ratios. The picture calls for little comment except perhaps to note the near-constancy of pitch-line film thickness when the wheel speed is used as the basic speed.

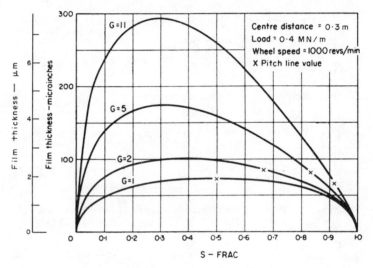

FIG. 13.2. Film thickness variation from base circle of wheel to base circle of pinion.

The last three figures present information which it is hoped will be of use to gear designers. Between them they give pitch line film thickness over a very wide range of operating conditions. Pitch line film thickness has been selected as characteristic because it is the only value of film thickness which is universally meaningful. The minimum and maximum values are dependent upon the specific tooth geometry. Typically the minimum value is about half the pitch line value for large gear ratios and roughly equal to the pitch line value for gear ratios near one, but for the present purpose the pitch line film thickness is adequately representative.

On the pitch line, $s = 0$, so

$$u = \frac{\pi N_1}{30} R_1 \sin \psi = \frac{\pi N_1}{30} \left(\frac{R_g l}{R_g + 1} \right) \sin \psi$$

$$R = \frac{R_g l}{(R_g + 1)^2} \sin \psi$$

$$h = \frac{k(\eta_0 u)^{0 \cdot 7} R^{0 \cdot 43}}{w^{0 \cdot 13}}$$

where

$$k = 1 \cdot 6 \alpha^{0 \cdot 6} (E^1)^{0 \cdot 03}$$

On the pitch line $h = h_p$, say, and so

$$h_p = k \frac{(l \sin \psi)^{1 \cdot 13}}{w^{0 \cdot 13}} \left(\frac{\eta_0 \pi N_1}{30} \right)^{0 \cdot 7} \frac{R_g^{1 \cdot 13}}{(R_g + 1)^{1 \cdot 56}}$$

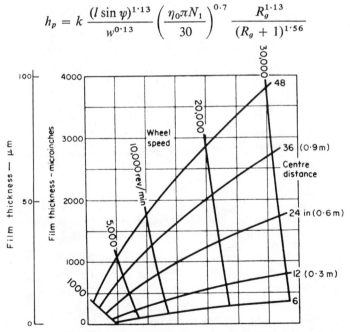

Fig. 13.3. Pitch line film thickness for gear ratio = 1, load = 0·4 MN/m, viscosity = 0·075 Pas.

Figures 13.3 and 13.4 are respectively course and fine carpet graphs of film thickness over a wide range of wheel and centre distances for a gear ratio of 1, a loading of 0·4 MN/m (1 ton/in.) face width and a viscosity of 0·075 Pas. Figure 13·5 gives correction factors for other values of viscosity, gear ratio

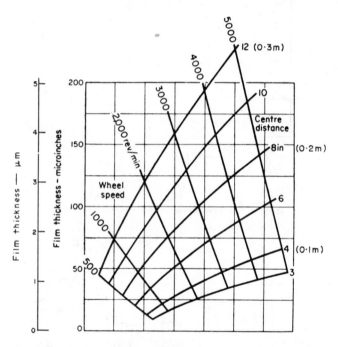

FIG. 13.4. Pitch-line film thickness for gear ratio = 1, load = 0·4 MN/m (1 ton/in.), viscosity = 0·075 Pas.

and tooth loading. To use these graphs, a film thickness is read off Fig. 13.3 or Fig. 13.4 for a particular wheel speed and centre distance and then corrected by multiplying by the factors given by Fig. 13.5 for the operating values of viscosity, gear ratio and load. The final value can be compared with the specified surface finish to give an indication of the likely extent of hydrodynamic lubrication. Experiments on disk machines suggest that the oil film effectively separates the solids if its calculated thickness exceeds the combined height of the irregularities of the two surface.

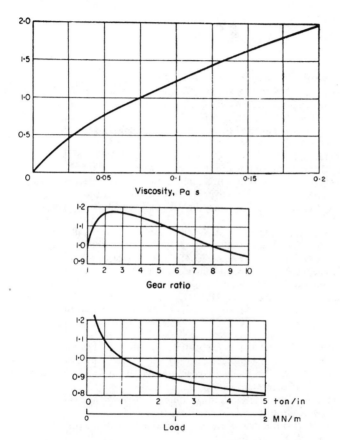

FIG. 13.5*. Correction factors for pitch-line film thickness.

* All the figures in this Chapter are reproduced from the *Proceedings of the Gear Lubrication Symposium*, 1964, by kind permission of the Institute of Petroleum.

REFERENCES

ALLAN, R. K. (1945) *Rolling Bearings*, Pitman.

AMER. SOC. MECH. ENGRS. (1953) Viscosity and density of over 40 fluids at pressures to 150,000 p.s.i. and temperatures to 425°F, Research Committee on Lubrication, A.S.M.E.

ARCHARD, J. F. (1959) The temperature of rubbing surfaces, *Wear*, 2, No. 6, 438.

ARCHARD, G. D., GAIR, F. C., and HIRST, W. (1961) The elasto-hydrodynamic lubrication of rollers, *Proc. Roy. Soc.* A 262, 51.

ARCHARD, J. F., HATCHER, B. G., and KIRK, M. T. (1964) Some experiments upon the behaviour of hypoid oils in heavily loaded contacts, Institution of Mechanical Engineers, Lubrication and Wear Convention, Paper No. 4.

ARCHARD, J. F. and KIRK, M. T. (1961) Lubrication at point contacts, *Proc. Roy. Soc.* A 261, 532.

ARCHARD, J. F. and KIRK, M. T. (1963), Influence of elastic modulus on the lubrication of point contacts, Institution of Mechanical Engineers, Lubrication and Wear Convention, Paper No. 15, p. 181.

ARCHARD, J. F. and KIRK, M. T. (1964) Film thicknesses for a range of lubricants under severe stress, *J. Mech. Engng. Sci.* 6, 101.

BARLOW, A. J. and LAMB, J. (1959) The visco-elastic behaviour of Lubrication oils, under Cyclic shearing stress, *Proc. Roy. Soc.* A 253, 52.

BELL, I. F. (1961) Elasto-hydrodynamic effects in lubrication, M. Sc. Thesis, University of Manchester.

BELL, J. C. (1962) Lubrication of rolling surfaces by a Ree–Eyring fluid, *Trans. Amer. Soc. Lub. Engrs.* 5, 160.

BLOK, H. (1950) Fundamental mechanical aspects of thin film lubrication, *Ann. N.Y. Acad. Sci.* 53, 779.

BLOK, H. (1952) Discussion. Gear Lubrication Symposium. Part I, The Lubrication of Gears, *J. Inst. Petrol.* 38, 673.

BLOK, H. (1959) Correlational review of theoretical and experimental data on elasto-hydrodynamic lubrication, Technische Hogeschol, Laboratorium voor Werktuigonderdelen, Delft, Holland.

BONDI, A. (1951) *Physical Chemistry of Lubricating Oils*, Reinhold, New York, 192.

224

BRIDGMAN, P.W. (1949) *The Physics of High Pressures*, Bell, London.

BRIX, V.H. (1947) Electrical study of boundary lubrication, *Aircr. Engng.*, **19**, 294.

BURTON, R.A. (1960) An analytical investigation of viscoelastic effects in the lubrication of rolling contact, *Trans. Amer. Soc. Lub. Engrs.* **3**, No. 1, 1.

BUTLER, L.H. (1960) The hydrodynamic effect between approaching surfaces with interposed viscous fluid films, and its influence on surface deformations, *J. Inst. Petrol.* **46**, No. 435, 63.

CAMERON, A. (1952) Hydrodynamic theory in gear lubrication, *J. Inst. Petrol.* **38**, 614.

CAMERON, A. (1954) Surface failure in gears, *J. Inst. Petrol.* **40**, 191.

CHENG, H.S. and STERNLICHT, B. (1964) A numerical solution for the pressure, temperature and film thickness between two infinitely long, lubricated rolling and sliding cylinders, under heavy loads, A.S.M.E. Paper No. 64, Lub. 11. Presented to the joint A.S.M.E.-A.S.L.E. International Lubrication Conference Washington D.C. 13–16 October 1964.

CHRISTENSEN, H. (1962) The oil film in a closing gap, *Proc. Roy. Soc.* A **266**, 312.

CHRISTENSEN, H. (1964a) Lubrication of highly loaded contacts, 4. SINTEF project 18.01.

CHRISTENSEN, H. (1964b) The variation of film thickness in highly loaded contacts, *A.S.L.E. Transactions* **7**, 219.

CROOK, A.W. (1957) Simulated gear-tooth contact: some experiments upon their lubrication and sub-surface deformations, *Proc. Inst. Mech. Engrs. London*. **171**, 187.

CROOK, A.W. (1958) The lubrication of rollers, I, *Phil. Trans.* A **250**, 387.

CROOK, A.W. (1961a) The lubrication of rollers, II, Film thickness with relation to viscosity and speed, *Phil. Trans.* A **254**, 223.

CROOK, A.W. (1961b) The lubrication of rollers, III, A theoretical discussion of friction and the temperatures in the oil film, *Phil. Trans.* A **254**, 237.

CROOK, A.W. (1961c) Elasto-hydrodynamic lubrication of rollers, *Nature*, **190**, 1182.

CROOK, A.W. (1963a) The lubrication of rollers, IV, Measurements of friction and effective viscosity, *Phil. Trans.* A **255**, 281.

CROOK, A.W. (1963b) Developments in elasto-hydrodynamic lubrication, *J. Inst. Petrol.* **49**, No. 478, 295.

DAWSON, P.H. (1961) The pitting of lubricated gear teeth and rollers, *Power Transmission*, **30**, No. 351, 208.

DAWSON, P. H. (1962) Effect of metallic contact on the pitting of lubricated rolling surfaces, *J. Mech. Engng. Sci.*, **4**, No. 1., 16.

DÖRR, J. (1954) Schmiermitteldruck and Randverformungen des Rollenlagers, *Ingenieur-Archiv*, **22**, No. 3, 171.

DOWSON, D. (1957) Investigation of cavitation in lubricating films supporting small loads, Inst. Mech. Engrs., Proc. of the Conference on Lubrication and Wear, Paper 49, 93.

DOWSON, D. and HIGGINSON, G. R. (1959) A numerical solution to the elastohydrodynamic problem, *J. Mech. Engng. Sci.*, **1**, No. 1, 6.

DOWSON, D. and HIGGINSON, G.R. (1961) New roller-bearing lubrication formula, *Engineering Lond.*, **192**, 158.

DOWSON, D. (1962) A generalized Reynolds equation for fluid-film lubrication, *Int. J. Mech. Sci.*, **4**, 159.

DOWSON, D., HIGGINSON, G.R. and WHITAKER, A.V. (1962) Elasto-hydrodynamic lubrication — a survey of isothermal solutions, *J. Mech. Engng. Sci.*, **4**, 2, 121.

DOWSON, D., HIGGINSON, G.R. and WHITAKER, A.V. (1963) Stress distribution in lubricated rolling contacts, Inst. Mech. Engrs. Symposium on Fatigue in Rolling Contact, Paper 6.

DOWSON, D. and HIGGINSON, G.R. (1963) The theory of roller bearing lubrication and deformation, Inst. Mech. Engrs. Lubrication and Wear Convention.

DOWSON, D. and HIGGINSON, G.R. (1964) A theory of involute gear lubrication, Inst. Pet. Gear Lubrication Symposium.

DOWSON, D. and LONGFIELD, M.D. (1963a) An elasto-hydrodynamic lubrication experiment, *Nature*, **197**, 586.

DOWSON, D. and LONGFIELD, M.D. (1963b) The distribution of pressure and temperature in a highly loaded lubricated contact, Inst. Mech. Engrs. Lubrication and Wear Convention.

DOWSON, D. and LONGFIELD, M.D. (1964) The lubrication of rolls of finite width: an investigation of oil-film characteristics. Paper No. 7. Third Annual Meeting of the Lubrication and Wear Group, The Institution of Mechanical Engineers. Cardiff 27–29 October 1964.

DOWSON, D. and WHITAKER, A.V. (1964) The isothermal lubrication of cylinders. Paper presented at the A.S.L.E./A.S.M.E. international Lubrication Conference, Washington D.C. 13–16 October 1964. A.S.L.E. Preprint No. 64-LC-22.

EL-SISI, S.I. and SHAWKI, G.S.A. (1960) Measurement of oil-film thickness between disks by electrical conductivity, *Trans. Amer. Soc. Mech. Engrs., J. of Basic Engineering* **82**, Series D, No. 1., 12.

EL-SISI, S.I. and SHAWKI, G.S.A. (1960) Performance characteristics of lubricating oil-film between disks, *Trans. Amer. Soc. Mech. Engrs., J. of Basic Engineering* **82**, Series D, No. 1., 19.

FLOBERG, L. (1961) Lubrication of two cylindrical surfaces, considering cavitation, *Transactions of Chalmers University of Technology*, **234**, No. 14. Institute of Machine Elements.

GALVIN, G.D., NAYLOR, H. and WILSON, A.R. (1964) The effect of pressure and temperature on some properties of fluids of importance in elasto-hydrodynamic lubrication, Instn. Mech. Engrs., Lubrication and Wear Second Convention.

GATCOMBE, E.K. (1945) Lubrication characteristics of involute spur-gears — a theoretical investigation, *Trans. Amer. Soc. Mech. Engrs.* **67**, 177.

GRUBIN, A.N. and VINOGRADOVA, I.E. (1949) Central Scientific Research Institute for Technology and Mechanical Engineering, Book No. 30, Moscow. (D.S.I.R. Translation No. 337).

HAGUE, B. (1945) *A-C Bridge Methods*, Pitman, London, 334.

HASHIMOTO, S. (1963) Experimental studies of the lubricating oil film between two rolling rollers, *Bulletin of J.S.M.E.*, **6**, No. 22. p. 327.

HASHIMOTO, S. (1964) Theoretical analysis of the oil film between rolling rollers, *Bulletin of J.S.M.E.* **7**, No. 26. p. 452.

HERSEY, M.D. and LOWDENSLAGER, D.B. (1950) Film thickness between gear teeth, *Trans. Amer. Soc. Mech. Engrs.*, **72**, 1035.

HIGGINSON, G.R. (1962) A model experiment in elasto-hydrodynamic lubrication, *Int. J. Mech. Sci.*, **4**, 205.

IIDA, K. and IGARASKI, A. (1959) On the behaviour of rollers in a cylindrical roller bearing, *Bulletin of J.S.M.E.*, **2**, 8, 538.

KANNEL, J.W., BELL, J.C. and ALLEN, C.M. (1964) Methods for determining pressure distribution in lubricated rolling contact, A.S.L.E. Paper No. 64 LC-24 Presented to the joint A.S.M.E.-A.S.L.E. International Lubrication Conference, Washington D.C. 13–16 October 1964.

KENYON, H.F. (1954) Brit. Pat. No. 777335.

KIRK, M.T. (1962) Hydrodynamic lubrication of Perspex, *Nature*, **194**, 965.

KODNIR, D.S. (1960) 'A General grapho-analytical and approximate method of solving the contact hydrodynamic problem' Trans. Third All-Union Conference on Friction and Wear. Ixdatel'stuo Akad. Naok SSSR, *3:* 58–66.

KOETS O.J. (1962) 'A Survey of the isothermal theory of elastohydro-dynamic lubrication', Univ. Technol. Rept. Delft.

KOROVCHINSKII, M.V. (1960) 'Some problems in the hydrodynamic theory of lubrication with deformation of the bodies bounding the lubricant film'. Third All Union Conference on Friction and Wear (Moscow) *3*, 74.

LANE, T.B. and HUGHES, J.R. (1952) A study of the oil film formation in gears by electrical resistance measurements, *Brit. J. Appl. Phys.*, **3**, 315.

LEWICKI, W. (1954) Hydrodynamic lubrication of roller bearings, *Engineer, Lond.* **197**, 920.

LEWICKI, W. (1955) Some physical aspects of lubrication in rolling bearings and gears, *Engineer, Lond.* **200**, 176, 212.

LOO, T.T. (1958) Effect of curvature on the Hertz theory for two circular cylinders in contact, *J. Appl. Mech.*, **25**, 122.

MACCONOCHIE, I.O. and CAMERON, A. (1960) The measurement of oil film thickness in gear teeth, *Trans. Amer. Soc. Mech. Engrs. J. of Basic Engineering*, Series D, **82**, 29.

MCEWEN, E. (1952) The effect of variation of viscosity with pressure on the load carrying capacity of oil films between gear teeth, *J. Inst. Petrol.* **38**, 646.

MARTIN, H.M. (1916) Lubrication of gear teeth, *Engineering, Lond.*, **102**, 199.

MELDAHL, A. (1941) Contribution to the theory of the lubrication of gears and of the stressing of the lubricated flanks of gear teeth, *Brown Boveri Review*, **28**, No. 11, 374.

MERRITT, H.E. (1935) Worm gear performance, *Proc. Instn. Mech. Engrs. Lond.* **129**, 127.

MERRITT, H.E. (1942) *Gears*, Pitman, London.

MERRITT, H.E. (1962) Gear-tooth contact phenomena, *Proc. Instn. Mech. Engrs.* Lond., **176**, No. 7., 141.

MILNE, A.A. (1957) A theory of rheodynamic lubrication for a Maxwell liquid, Instn. Mech. Engrs., Proc. of the Conference on Lubrication and Wear, Paper 41, 66.

MISHARIN, J.A. (1958) Influence of the friction conditions on the magnitude of the friction coefficient in the case of rolling with sliding, Instn. Mech. Engrs., Proc of the International Conference on Gearing, Paper 40, 159.

NIEMANN, G. and GARTNER, F. (1964) Distribution of hydrodynamic pressure on counterformal line contacts, A.S.L.E. Paper No. 64 LC-12, Presented to the joint A.S.M.E.-A.S.L.E. International Lubrication Conference, Washington D.C. 13–16 October 1964.

OSTERLE, J.F. (1959) On the hydrodynamic lubrication of roller bearings, *Wear*, **2**, No. 3, 195.

OSTERLE, J.F. and SAIBEL, E. (1957) Surface deformations in the hydro-dynamic slider-bearing problem and their effect on the pressure development, Instn. Mech. Engrs., Proc. of the Conference on Lubrication and Wear, Paper 35, 53.

OSTERLE, J.F. and STEPHENSON, R.R. (1962) A direct solution of the elasto-hydrodynamic lubrication problem, *Trans. Amer. Soc. Lub. Engrs.*, **5**, No. 2, 365.

PAI, S.I. (1956) *Viscous Flow Theory, I-Laminar Flow*, D. Van Nostrand Company Inc., New Jersey.

PALMGREN, A. (1945) *Ball and Roller Bearing Engineering* (S.K.F. Industries) Burbank.

PEPPLER, W. (1936) Untersuchungen über die Druckübertragung bei belasteten und geschmierten umlaufenden achsparallelen Zylindern, Maschinenelemente-Tagung Aachen 1935, 42; *V.D.I. Verlag, Berlin*, 1936.

PEPPLER, W. (1938) Druckübertragung an geschmierten zylindrischen Gleit-und Wälzflächen, *V.D.I.-Forschungsheft* 391.

PEPPLER, W. (1957) Die Theorie der hydrodynamischen Schmierung unter besonderer Berücksichtigung physikalischer Erweiterungen, *V.D.I.-Be-richte*, **20**, 13, 183.

PETRUSEVICH, A.I. (1951) Fundamental conclusions from the contact—hydrodynamic theory of lubrication, *Izo. Akad. Nauk SSSR (OTN)* 2, 209.

PORITSKY, H. (1950) Stresses and deflections of cylindrical bodies in contact with application to contact of gears and of locomotive wheels, *J. Appl. Mech., Trans. Amer. Soc. Mech. Engrs.* **72**, 191.

PORITSKY, H. (1952) Lubrication of gear teeth, including the effect of elastic displacement. First Amer. Soc. Lub. Engrs. National Symposium, (Fundamentals of Friction and Lubrication in Engineering). Chicago, 98.

PURDAY, H.F.P. (1949) *Streamline Flow*, Constable, London.

REE, T. and EYRING, H. (1955) Theory of non-Newtonian flow. I. Solid plastic system, and theory of non-Newtonian flow. II. Solution system of high polymers. *J. Appl. Phys.* **26**, (7), 793–800 (Part I) and 800–809 (Part II).

REYNOLDS, O. (1886) On the theory of lubrication and its application to Mr. Beauchamp Tower's experiments, *Phil. Trans.* **177**, 157.

SASAKI, T., MORI, H. and OKINO, N. (1962) Fluid lubrication theory of roller bearings. *Trans. Amer. Soc. Mech. Engrs. J. of Basic Engineering*, **84**, Series D, No. 1, Part I, 166. Part II, 175.

SIBLEY, L.B., BELL, J.C., ORCUTT, F.K. and ALLEN, C.M. (1960) A study of the influence of lubricant properties on the performance of aircraft gas turbine engine rolling-contact bearings, WADD Technical Report, 60–189.

SIBLEY, L.B. and ORCUTT, F.K. (1961) Elasto-hydrodynamic lubrication of rolling contact surfaces, *Trans. Amer. Soc. Lub. Engrs.* **4**, (2), 234.

SMITH, C.F. (1962) Some aspects of the performance of high-speed lightly loaded cylindrical roller bearings, Inst. Mech. Engrs., Lubrication and Wear Group.

SMITH, F.W. (1959) Lubricant behaviour in concentrated contact systems — the castor oil — steel system, *Wear,* **2**, No. 4, 250.

SMITH, F.W. (1960) Lubricant behaviour in concentrated contact — some rheological problems, *Trans. Amer. Soc. Lub. Engrs.* **3**, No. 1, 18.

SMITH, F.W. (1961) Rolling contact lubrication in relation to wear research, paper presented to A.S.M.E. Research Committee on Lubrication, Battelle, Memorial Institute, Columbus, Ohio, (Sept.).

SMITH, F.W. (1962) The effect of temperature in concentrated contact lubrication, *Trans. Amer. Soc. Lub. Engrs.* **5**, 142.

STERNLICHT, B., LEWIS, P. and FLYNN, P. (1961) Theory of lubrication and failure of rolling contacts, *Trans. Amer. Soc. Mech. Engrs., J. of Basic Engineering* **83**, Series D, 2, 213.

TALLIAN, T.E., CHIU, Y.P. HUTTENLOCHER, D.F., KAMENSHIRE, J.A., SIBLEY, L.B. and SINDLINGER, N.E. (1964) Lubricant films in rolling contact of rough surfaces, *Trans. Amer. Soc. Lub. Engrs.* **7**, 109.

TANNER, R.I. (1960) Full-film lubrication theory for a Maxwell liquid. *Int. J. Mech. Sci.* **1**. 206.

WEBER, C. and SAALFELD, K. (1954) Schmierfilm bei Walzen mit Verformung, *Zeits. ang. Math. Mech.* **34** (Nos. 1–2), 54.

AUTHOR INDEX

231

SUBJECT INDEX

233